GW00374893

A Guide to the
LLOYD'S MARINE COLLECTION
and
Related Marine Sources
at
Guildhall Library

Compiled by
D.T. Barriskill

GUILDHALL LIBRARY
SECOND (REVISED) EDITION
1994

PREFACE TO THE SECOND EDITION

Since the arrival of the Lloyd's Marine Collection at Guildhall Library in May 1979, the use made of it and the recognition of its importance have increased considerably. Parallel with this expansion in its use has been the additional amount of records that have been passed onto the Collection from the Corporation of Lloyd's. The interest generated by the Collection and the need to further utilise it has meant the decision to include other maritime sources at Guildhall Library and elsewhere in a new edition of the *Guide*.

The first edition was compiled by C. A. Hall and his labours still represent the central theme and structure of the revised *Guide*. When the Collection came to Guildhall Library, it became his responsibility not just to care for the records but to produce a comprehensive and instructive manual in respect of the Collection. Thus the new edition is still very much in his debt.

The new edition has also benefitted from the enthusiasm and interest shown in it by Miss Jenny Wraight. Her advice and extensive knowledge of the Lloyd's Marine Collection has been much used in compiling the second edition. Indeed she it was who realised the need for a new *Guide* and took the first steps towards that stage.

I hope that users of the revised *Guide* will find that it reflects the changes that have taken place since 1979, and that errors will be as minimal as possible.

D.T. Barriskill
1994.

CONTENTS

Introduction:

Historical Note

Part One — A description of the Lloyd's Marine Collection

Part Two – Making a Search

INTRODUCTION

'Can you tell me about the ship which was sunk by butterflies?' This is one of the more bizarre enquiries that we have received since the Lloyd's Marine Collection came to Guildhall Library in May 1979. (It seems that it is something of a chestnut in the world of maritime history and so far no one has come up with any documentary evidence that the incident ever occurred!) The majority of enquiries, though often fascinating, are more mundane. They concern the every-day events of shipping during the past two-and-a-half centuries: sailings and arrivals, shipwrecks and the careers of captains. They come from marine and local historians, archaeologists, amateur divers and professional salvors and, most of all, from people with family connections with those who sailed in the ships as passengers or crew. This guide is intended to provide a detailed descrip-tion of the sources to be found in the Collection. We have also included, in Part Two, some suggestions as to how the Collection may be used and the where-abouts of other records, such as passenger and crew lists and pictures, which are not available here.

The Collection was deposited at the Library on permanent loan in 1979. It com-prises the historical marine records of the Corporation of Lloyd's and includes both printed and manuscript material. Current files (covering approximately ten years) are retained by Lloyd's, and when the Collection first came here the cut-off date for the majority of it was 1970. Since then there have been further deposits and most current series now come up to within 5 to 10 years. An impor-tant addition to the Collection was made in 1981 when microfilms of the post-1920 records of Lloyd's Confidential Index were deposited. As the more recent records include information which is still confidential there is a 30 year embargo on their use. In 1982 some parts of the Collection (mainly the publications of organisations other than Lloyd's) were given to the Library outright.

Guildhall Library is, as many readers will be aware, a library devoted principally to the history of London and to the local and family history of other parts of England. The presence of the Lloyd's Marine Collection and the large number of enquiries which it has generated have led the staff into fresh fields and we would like to record our appreciation of the efforts of the former Librarian of Lloyd's, Mr. T.M. Dinan, in setting us on the right path and helping us from time to time as we have settled into our stride. Any errors that may appear in this guide are, however, our own. While we have tried as far as possible to make it complete and accurate there are sure to be some, and it is also likely that there are less-used parts of the Collection of which the potential has not been fully realised. We would welcome any suggestions which might help to improve future editions.

HISTORICAL NOTE

The great insurance market of Lloyd's traces its origins back to a coffee house opened by Edward Lloyd, probably towards the end of 1688. In its early years, first in Tower Street and later in new premises in Lombard Street, Lloyd's Coffee House increased its reputation as a centre of commercial activity, and by the time of its founder's death in 1713 had become firmly established. Its special association with Marine insurance developed gradually during the eighteenth century and it was not until 1760 that the underwriters who frequented Lloyd's first combined in a formal association. This was a society founded to organise the production and publication of a Register Book of Shipping to guide its members in their decisions, the first issue of which appeared in 1764.

The newly-organised professional underwriters were concerned by the influx of speculative insurers, who were little more than gamblers, and in 1769 they founded a New Lloyd's Coffee House in Pope's Head Alley. Although the old Lloyd's Coffee House survived into the 1780s it was the new one from which the present Lloyd's grew. The accommodation at the new coffee house soon became inadequate for the increasingly professional market and in 1771 the first Committee of Lloyd's was formed to raise a subscription for the provision of better facilities. Three years later Lloyd's moved into rooms at the Royal Exchange, where it remained until 1928, apart from a short break (1838-44) after the old Royal Exchange building was burned down.

The first move to control the market was made in 1778 when admission to Lloyd's was restricted to Subscribers and their connections, but by the early years of the nineteenth century it had become apparent that a systematic reorganisation would be necessary. Accordingly, in 1811 a series of by-laws was drawn up and Subscribers were required to sign a Trust Deed binding them to the Society's rules and regulations. Thereafter the history of Lloyd's is one of developing sophistication in the insurance business and the services provided for underwriters. In 1834, following a long period during which two rival Register Books were published, a new Society, Lloyd's Register of British and Foreign Shipping, was formed to supervise surveys and publish *Lloyd's Register of Shipping*. This Society was, and is, independent of Lloyd's, a fact which continues to be the source of some confusion. Lloyd's was incorporated in 1871 under the first of a series of Lloyd's Acts (the most recent being that of 1982).

In 1928 Lloyd's moved into a new building in Leadenhall Street. Within thirty years these premises had become inadequate and a second building was constructed in Lime Street and occupied in 1958. By 1979 the accommodation available in the two buildings had again become insufficient and the 1928 one was demolished in order to make way for a third Lloyd's building, which was completed in 1986.

Edward Lloyd published a general news-sheet, *Lloyd's News*, between September 1696 and February 1697. Publication came to an abrupt end when an inaccurate report of proceedings in the House of Lords appeared, apparently inserted by the printer. Since such reporting, even if accurate, was regarded at the time as a breach of parliamentary privilege, Lloyd evidently decided that he would not risk a, perhaps more serious, recurrence of the incident. The publishing history of Lloyd's really begins with the first appearance of *Lloyd's List*, probably in April 1734. The first surviving issue dates from 2 January 1740/1 and includes both general commercial information and details of vessels arriving at ports in England and Ireland. Other issues of the period include information on shipping arrivals in other parts of the world. This information came from correspondents with whom the proprietors of Lloyd's had made contact: the worldwide network of Lloyd's agents, on whose reports the content of *Lloyd's List* is now based, has been built up since 1811. Later developments in the history of *Lloyd's List* are described in Part One, Section 11. In 1973, Lloyd's of London Press Ltd. was formed as a wholly-owned subsidiary to handle all the news-gathering and publishing activities of the Corporation of Lloyd's. The other major publication which began life in Lloyd's Coffee House is *Lloyd's Register of Shipping*, the origins of which go back to the Register Book published in 1764. Further information may be found in Part One, Section 1.

Readers interested in the history of Lloyd's are referred to *A History of Lloyd's* by Charles Wright and Charles Ernest Fayle (1928) and *Annals of Lloyd's Register* (1934). References to other books and articles on Lloyd's will be found in the London Subject Catalogue in the Printed Books Reading Room at the number L64.9.

PART ONE —

THE LLOYD'S MARINE COLLECTION

Only the parts of the Collection held by the Manuscripts Section have so far been fully catalogued. The rest of the Collection, held by the Printed Books Section, is not included in the catalogue in the Printed Books Reading Room. No attempt has been made in this guide to offer a formal catalogue of the Collection.

The entries in Part One are, as far as possible, arranged in the following manner. The most usual form of the title (generally, in the case of a current series, the one in current use) is taken as the heading. Details of holdings are given, beginning with dates covered and followed, where appropriate, by a list of variant titles. Other related publications in the Collection are noted. The descriptive text generally begins with a note on publication history, in which the information on dates and titles may be expanded and clarified, followed by a description of contents and a note on the physical form of the source (e.g. number of volumes per year). At least forty eight hours' notice is required for access to information in certain card indexes, as indicated in the appropriate sections.

The majority of the Collection is held by the Printed Books Section and enquiries and requests should be addressed to the Printed Books Enquiry Desk except where otherwise indicated.

1. Lloyd's Register

1764 (updated in manuscript to 1766), 1768 M-Z (updated in manuscript to 1771), 1775-84, 1786-7, 1789-1802, 1803 (Green Book only), 1804-6, 1807 (Green Book only), 1808-16, 1818 to date minus 2 years.

The Register of Shipping, 1764-1833 (Green Book only, 1800-1810).
The New Register Book of Shipping, 1800-1810 (Red Book only).
Lloyd's Register of British and Foreign Shipping, 1834-1913/14.
Lloyd's Register of Shipping, 1914/15-1948/9.
Lloyd's Register of Shipping, *Register Book*, 1949/50-1974/5.
Lloyd's Register of Shipping, *Register of Ships*, 1975/6 to date minus 2 years.

The first surviving issue of *Lloyd's Register* dates from 1764, and the second, of which only the latter part is extant, from 1768. Both were updated in manuscript. The next issue to survive is that from 1775 and thereafter the file is continuous, apart from the years 1785, 1788 and 1817. Between 1800 and 1833, as a result of a dispute within the shipping community, two separate register books were published, one by a society consisting mainly of shipowners (known as the 'Red Book') and the other by a society of underwriters (the 'Green Book'). Their coverage is similar but not precisely the same, some vessels being included by one society and not the other. *Lloyd's Register* for the years 1764 to 1833 is available in the Lloyd's Marine Collection in the facsimile reprint edition published by the Gregg Press. Subsequent volumes are the original editions. Together they represent a complete file of issues known to have survived, apart from the most recent ones which have not yet been passed to the Library.

Lloyd's Register is an annual list of vessels, giving details current at the time of publication. The following table shows the main categories of information published, together with the dates between which each appeared:

Name of vessels...1764—date

Previous names (if any) ....1764—date

Official number ....1872/3—date

Signal code...1874/5—date

Rig/description ....1768—date

Tonnage ....1764—date

    gross, net and under-deck ....1874/5—date

Dimensions:

    load-draught ....1775—1833

    length, breadth and depth..1863—date

Description of engines..1874/5—date

Date of building..1764—date*

Place of building...1764—date

Name of builder..1860—date

Name of owner ....1764—date

Name of master.....................1764 to 1920/1. To 1947 in Sailing Vessel Register

    dates of service with owner/on vessel ....1887—1920/1

Number of crew ....1764—1771

Port of registry ....1834—date

Port of survey ....1764—date

Class...1764—date

'Postings' of casualties, etc ....1775—1966/7

Destined voyage...1764-1873/4

*Green Book, 1800-33, gives age.

Until 1890 *Lloyd's Register* was almost exclusively confined to British registered vessels, although some foreign vessels which traded regularly with the United Kingdom were listed. Apart from a brief period from 1834 to 1837 (during which all British vessels of 50 tons and over were included) only after 1875 were vessels which had not been surveyed and classed by Lloyd's introduced into the *Register*. In 1875 other British vessels of 100 tons and over were added and since 1890 all British and foreign sea-going merchant vessels over 100 tons have been included.

Until 1890 the main part of *Lloyd's Register*, the list of vessels, appeared as a single alphabetical sequence, with supplementary pages at the end (or in the case of the Red Book, 1800 to 1833, at the end of each section) in which vessels newly-registered or renamed since publication were added. Since 1890 several changes have been made, although the supplementary pages continued to be used until 1973/4. Between 1890 and 1947 sailing vessels and steamers (together, latterly, with motor vessels) were listed separately. An additional section for trawlers and other fishing vessels (after 1932, all steamers and motor vessels under 300 tons), bound in with the list of sailing vessels, was introduced in 1922. In 1948 the three categories were reunited in a single alphabetical sequence.

Between 1775 and 1954/5 the set of *Lloyd's Register* in the Lloyd's Marine Collection is 'posted' with details of casualties etc. Early postings generally consist of the single word 'wrecked' entered against the name of a lost ship. Later, from 1890, notes of vessels missing and broken up were included, together with the month and year expressed in figures (e.g. 'Broken up 6.92'). Other alterations such as changes of master, ownership, port of registration or vessel's name, are similarly noted. In the case of a name change there is usually a reference to the supplementary pages at the end of the volume, where full details may be found.

Numerous appendices have been published in *Lloyd's Register*, including statistical information, specialised lists of vessels and particulars of shipbuilders and owners. Amongst the most useful are the lists of changes of name (1876/7 onwards) and indexes to compound names (1890/1 onwards), and the lists of shipowners and their fleets (1876/7 onwards) and shipbuilders and their existing vessels (1890/1 onwards). Other series which may be of interest include the following: lists of the Royal Navy (1779-83) and of 'warships of the world' (1890/1-94/5); lists of East India Company ships (1778-1833); lists of steam vessels (1839-54) and of ships built of iron (1843-54); lists of refrigerated vessels (1896/7 onwards), tankers (1896/7 onwards) and off-shore oil installations (1969/70 onwards); and lists of qualified masters and mates who had passed examinations to gain their certificates (1846-52). These latter are a useful supplement to the 'Captains registers' (see Section 36) which they predate, but it should be borne in mind that only a minority of masters and mates active at that time would have taken examinations and it is only these who are included. A complete list of the appendices published in *Lloyd's Register* is available for consultation at the Printed Books Enquiry Desk.

Note: since 1834 *Lloyd's Register* has been published in the middle of the year, covering the following period of I July to 30 June. However, until 1868 the spines of the volumes in the Collection were lettered with the date of publication, and only since the 1869/70 issue have both years covered been shown. In ordering books it is therefore customary to refer to the earlier volumes by the single date of publication, e.g. ' 1850', and to the later ones by the years covered, e.g. '1895/6'. Between 1893/4 and 1947/8 the sections on steamers and sailing vessels are bound separately. Since the 1947/8 issue, when the sections were recombined, this part of *Lloyd's Register* has appeared in two volumes divided alphabetically, except between 1955/6 and 1965/6 when it was published in a single volume. The appendices, apart (until 1956/7) from the lists of shipowners, have been published as a separate volume since 1890/1. Between 1940/1 and 1946/7 there was no appendix volume published.

Owing to the difficulties experienced in classing iron and steel hulls, many of the early steamships are absent from *Lloyd's Register*. However, they may be found in the *Mercantile Navy List* or in the various returns of British registered steamships which were recorded in the Parliamentary Papers (PP). The first of these covering 1814-28 inclusive can be found in PP 1829 vol. 17. Later returns are in PP 1830 vol. 31, 1835 vol. 48, 1845 vol. 47, 1851 vol. 52, 1852 vol. 49, 1854 vol. 60 and 1854/5 vol. 46. The series continued until 1870, but after 1857 it is easier to consult the *Mercantile Navy List*, as the returns were arranged by port and not indexed by ship.

2. Lloyd's Register Casualty Returns

1890-1980.

Returns of Vessels totally Lost, Condemned etc., 1890-23.
Returns of Ships totally Lost, Condemned etc., 1923-37.
Returns of Ships totally Lost, Broken up, etc., 1937 49.
Merchant Ships totally Lost, Broken Up, etc., 1950-66.
Casualty Returns . . ., 1967-80.

Sometimes referred to as 'Lloyd's Register Wreck Returns', from the title of the statistical tables in earlier issues. Quarterly returns made by Lloyd's Register of Shipping, giving statistics and details of vessels of 100 tons and over removed from *Lloyd's Register*. The latter are arranged by category ('Burnt', 'Collision' etc.). Until the third quarter of 1975, when alphabetical order was adopted, each section had British vessels placed first, followed by those of other nationalities. Annual statistical summaries are also published, which include addenda to the lists of casualties and, since 1950, an index covering the year. The spines of these volumes are labelled 'Lloyd's Register Wreck Returns', and this title should be used when ordering them.

3. Lloyd's Register of Yachts

1919-39, 1947-1980.

Lloyd's Register of Yachts was established in 1878, but the file in the Lloyd's Marine Collection commences in 1920. No issues were published in the years 1940 to 1946 inclusive. A Supplement to the 1939 Yacht Register was produced in 1946 however. Publication of the _Register_ ceased altogether in 1980, but _Lloyd's Register_ has produced an annual list of those yachts classed by _Lloyd's Register_ since 1981.

The yacht register is complementary to _Lloyd's Register of Shipping_ and is similarly arranged. It covers yachts of all nationalities (except those covered by _Lloyd's Register of American Yachts_; see Section 4) in the following categories: yachts classed by Lloyd's Register; yachts owned by subscribers to the yacht register; and certain other yachts above a specified size (recently a sail area of 350 square feet or more and/or a minimum length of 27 feet). In addition to particulars of the vessels themselves, the yacht register includes lists of owners, builders and designers and the principal yacht clubs of the world. Issues from 1920 to 1960 have colour plates of yacht club flags and those from 1922 to 1960 illustrations of the distinguishing flags of yachts and yachtsmen.

4. Lloyd's Register of American Yachts

1929-42. 1947-77.

Lloyd's Register of American Yachts was established in 1903, but the file in the Lloyd's Marine Collection commences in 1929. No issues were published in the years 1943 to 1946 inclusive and publication ceased altogether in 1978. Similar to _Lloyd's Register of Yachts_ it covers United States' and Canadian vessels. Until 1932 West Indian and South American vessels were also included.

5. Mercantile Navy List

1857-1940, 1947-76 (with monthly supplements 1947-77).

It has now been succeeded by the Department of Trade _Official List of Registered Ships_.

Mercantile Navy List and Annual Appendage to the Commercial Code of Signals for All Nations, 1857-64.
Mercantile Navy List and Maritime Directory, 1865-1957.
Mercantile Navy List, 1958 onwards.

also _British Code List_, 1869, 1871 and 1900.

The _Mercantile Navy List_ was the official list of British-registered merchant vessels, published for the Registrar General of Shipping and Seamen. It first appeared in 1850 (corrected to December 1849), although the earliest in the Collection dates from 1857, and ceased publication with the 1977 issue. The main categories of information included are shown in the following table (cf similar table for _Lloyd's Register_ on page 5).

Name of vessel ....1857—date

Official number ....1857—date

Signal code ....1857—date

Rig* ....1872—date

Tonnage ....1857—date

   registered (net)..1857—date

   gross and net§ ....1871—date

Dimensions§..1871—1957

Construction materials§ ....1871—date

Horsepower§ ....1871—1957

Description of propeller (ie screw or paddle)§ ....1871—1921

Date of building...1871—date

Place of building..1871—date

Name and address of owner ....1865—date

Port of registry..1857—date

Year of registration§ ....1871—date

*sailing vessels only
§steamers and motor vessels only.

Apart from the period between 1858 and 1864, during which some foreign vessels were included in appendices, the *Mercantile Navy List* was exclusively confined to British vessels (see below) including those registered at overseas ports within the British Empire and, more recently, the Commonwealth.

Between 1857 and 1864 the *Mercantile Navy List* comprised a list of vessels in order of their official numbers, with an alphabetical index. Subsequently the numerical list was abandoned, to be replaced, between 1865 and 1870, by a single alphabetical sequence. In 1871 this was split into two (steamers and sailing vessels) and in 1922 three (sailing vessels, steamers and motor vessels). The 1869 and 1871 issues have copies of the *British Code List* bound in. These list British vessels in alphabetical order of signal code. There is a separate copy of the *British Code List* 1900.

Like *Lloyd's Register*, the *Mercantile Navy List* includes a number of appendices, most of them published only for short periods. Among them are lists of the Royal Navy and the East India Company Navy/HM Indian Navy (1857-64, 1869 and 1871), of American naval and merchant vessels (1860-64) and of foreign vessels 'to which special signals have been appropriated' (1858-64). Between 1875, and 1904 lists of vessels removed from the register while the current issue was going through the press, giving reasons for removal, were included.

Between 1857 and 1864 the *Mercantile Navy List* includes lists of the holders of masters' and mates' certificates, pilots, receivers of wreck, British consuls abroad and, in 1863 and 1864 only, officers of the Royal Naval Reserve. These early editions (1857-64) also include annual obituary lists and cumulative lists of officers who had received awards and testimonials for exceptional services at sea, usually in connection with shipwrecks. The entries in the latter are not always dated, but the majority relate to the period c.1838 to c.1862.

Note: Until 1957 the *Mercantile Navy List* was published as a single volume. After that date it appeared in two loose-leaf binders, Part One covering sail and steam and Part Two motor vessels.

See also section below.

6. Registrar General's Monthly Returns

1890-1946.

The monthly returns of the Registrar General of Shipping and Seamen, published by HMSO under a variety of titles. Each issue contains statistics and lists of British vessels added to or removed from the register, with explanations. The Returns act as a monthly Supplement to the *Mercantile Navy List* and are particularly useful in tracing the fate of vessels that were broken up rather than wrecked, sold or renamed. From 1947 the Returns were replaced by the Monthly Supplements to the MNL.

7. Department of Trade Official List of Registered Ships 1979 and 1980

Each volume is split into two parts. Part One is an alphabetical list of Merchant and Fishing vessels. Each entry comprises official number, name of ship, port of registry, type, gross/net tons and registered owner. Part Two is also an alphabetical list but is confined to those vessels reported as registered in a number of ports of smaller British possessions.

The *Official List* replaced the defunct *Mercantile Navy List*. It excludes pleasure craft and fishing boats under 15 tons net.

8. Olsen's Fisherman's Almanack

1981, 1984 and 1985.

This almanack was first issued in 1876. It is a useful guide to tide tables, port facilities, light houses and light vessels for the U.K., Eire and some other European countries. More importantly it contains a list of British fishing vessels over 15 tons gross. At present there are only issues for three years in the library.

9. American Bureau of Shipping Record

1913-19, 1921-64, 1966-80.

Has been transferred to the National Maritime Museum, Greenwich.

10. Merchant Vessels of the United States

1913, 1915-16, 1918-39, 1941, 1943-65, 1968-80.

Has been transferred to the National Maritime Museum, Greenwich.

11. Lloyd's List

1741, 1744, 1747-53, 1755, 1757-8, 1760 77, 1779 to date minus three months.

Lloyd's List, 1741-70, 1772 (see also below).
New Lloyd's List, 1771, 1773-88.
Lloyd's List, 1789-1871 (continuation of *New Lloyd's List*).
Lloyd's List and *Commercial Daily Chronicle*, 1872-June 1884.
Shipping and Mercantile Gazette and Lloyd's List, July 1884 1 June 1914.
Lloyd's List, July 1914 to date minus three months

The first surviving issue of *Lloyd's List* is dated '2 January 1740', i.e., by modern reckoning, 1741. In 1769 a rival 'New Lloyd's Coffee House' was established and began publication of the *New Lloyd's List*, the earliest surviving issue of which dates from 1771. The two titles ran concurrently for several years, surviving from alternate years for the period 1770 to 1773. From 1773 onwards only the *New Lloyd's List* survives, although the 'New' was dropped from the title after 1788. Publication remained in the hands of Lloyd's until July 1884 when *Lloyd's List* was amalgamated with the *Shipping and Mercantile Gazette* (which had been published since 1838), Lloyd's continuing to supply details of movements and casualties. This arrangement continued until June 1914, after which Lloyd's reassumed responsibility for publication. Since 1973 *Lloyd's List* has been published by Lloyd's of London Press Ltd.

Lloyd's List was originally a weekly, but was published twice a week for a hundred years until 1 July 1837 since when it has appeared daily, Monday to Saturday.

Lloyd's List is used primarily as a source of information on shipping movements and casualties and the sections covering these have altered only slightly since 1741. Movements are arranged 'geographically' by port, beginning with Gravesend (i.e. London) and then proceeding clockwise round the British Isles and similarly round other regions of the world. Under each heading arrivals and sailings are listed separately in chronological order. Each entry usually includes the date, the name of the vessel, the name of her master and the port from which she has come or for which she has sailed. Casualty reports and other items of news originally appeared in apparently random order. Subsequently they were arranged under the ports from which the reports were received and towards the end of the nineteenth century the present arrangement, alphabetical by vessel's name, was adopted. 'Speakings' (i.e. reports of communications between ships at sea) are listed separately.

Unlike *Lloyd's Register*, *Lloyd's List* has never been confined to British vessels nor to those surveyed by Lloyd's. Until the early nineteenth century references to the movements of Royal Naval vessels may be found, although these were subsequently dropped. It follows that it is often possible to trace references to the movements of vessels which are not included in *Lloyd's Register*.

Until the mid nineteenth century the emphasis in reporting movements was on arrivals. Many, but probably not all, sailings from London were reported, as were some from other major British ports, but those from lesser and foreign ports rarely appear. Subsequently *Lloyd's List* offers a more comprehensive record.

Before the introduction of telegraphic communications casualty reports were usually brief and often vague in content. There was seldom more than one relating to each incident. By the 1880s reporting had become much quicker and on-the-spot reports from Lloyd's agents were often published verbatim, giving a much more detailed account of events. These sometimes include details of cargoes and lives lost and of salvage attempts immediately following the loss.

During the latter part of the First and the whole of the Second World War the shipping movements and casualties sections were printed separately from the remainder of *Lloyd's List* and distributed on a very restricted basis. The volumes for the First World War are entitled *Oversea Shipping Intelligence* and those for the Second *Lloyd's List: Confidential Movements* and they cover, respectively, 1 January 1917 to 15 November 1918 and 30 August 1939 to 15 September 1945. Both are now on microfilm in the Printed Books Reading Room and they may also be purchased from the Bookshop either in part or in whole.

During the nineteenth and early twentieth centuries *Lloyd's List* was expanded to include additional shipping information and more general commercial news. The principal categories of information are as follows:

Customs

London:
ships entered inwards   July 1837—November 1969
ships entered outwards   July 1837—November 1969
ships cleared outwards   July 1837—November 1969
sailing vessels (later all vessels)
entered outwards at Customs House for
foreign ports   May 1838—June 1914

Liverpool:
vessels (later only sailing vessels)
entered outwards for foreign ports   March 1854—June 1914

Clyde:
sailing vessels entered outwards
for foreign ports   April 1854—June 1914

Docks and loading
London loading list   December 1837—April 1838
Ships loading directory/list (London
and later other ports)   1875—1929
London dock directory   1872—January 1922
Ships in port (UK)   1923 onwards

Movements
Homeward bound vessels   1872—74, 1884—1916
Outward bound vessels   1884—1916
Ships expected at UK ports   1923 onwards
Movements of British vessels (A-Z)   1923—August 1939

Special categories
Colliers: London, entered inwards   July 1837—July 1838
Coasters: London, entered inwards   July 1837—July 1838
London, entered outwards   July 1837—July 1838
coasting trade (i.e. movements)   1884—1916, 1922 onwards
Liner sailings (weekly announcements)   1925—May 1935

Other information
Salvage: Receivers' reports   October 1846—
Salvage Association reports   February 1870—
Log extracts   1902—1916
Ice reports   April 1913—1916
Derelicts and wreckage   April 1882—1916
Launches   March 1908 onwards

Many of these series appear occasionally, either on set days in the week or irregularly. They are not covered by the indexes. The news items (1880 onwards) include reports of Board of Trade inquiries, information on trade disputes, wars etc. affecting commerce, and general shipping and commercial news.

The indexes to *Lloyd's List* are described in the next section.

Note: the volumes of *Lloyd's List* in this collection are bound as follows:

1741-1836, one volume per year
1837-53, half-yearly
1854 June 1884, quarterly
(July 1884-August 1919, microfilm only)
September 1919-1951, quarterly
1952 onwards, bi-monthly.
Gregg Press reprints: 1741-1818, two years per volume
1819-1826, one volume per year.

In the interests of conserving the original volumes, readers are asked to use the Gregg Press facsimile reprints of the volumes for the period 1741 to 1826. Issues for the period 1827 to August 1919 are available only on microfilm. Copies for the years September 1919 to 1975 can be seen in hard copy and 1976 onwards on microfilm.

For the duration of the Great War a separate list: *Confidential Movements of Vessels on Government Service 1914-1918* was produced. This is available on microfilm in the Printed Books Reading Room.

12. Lloyd's List Indexes

Casualties and 'paragraphs' (i.e. news items): 1741-63, 1767-8, 1770-1, 1775-6, 1779, 1783 (indexes of other years up to 1799 in progress).
Movements and casualties: 1838-1927.
News: c.1920-c.1970 (48 hours' notice required).

see also *Voyage record cards* (1927-c.1975) (Section 13).

Indexes to casualty and other miscellaneous reports (not movements) appearing in some of the eighteenth century volumes of *Lloyd's List* have been prepared. Typescript copies of these indexes have been placed in the volumes to which they refer. A project to index the remaining eighteenth century volumes is in progress: please enquire at the Printed Books Enquiry Desk for information on newly-indexed volumes.

Shipping movements are indexed from 1838 onwards. The main series of annual indexes runs from 1838 to 1927 and originally took the form of manuscript volumes, although, with the exception of five sample volumes (see Section 40), it now survives only on microfilm. The films are kept in the cabinet in the Printed Books Reading Room.

The indexes, each of which covers the period of one year, include references to reports of arrivals, sailings, speakings and casualties. The arrangement is alphabetical by name of vessel, with similar names grouped together. Steamers are distinguished by the abbreviation '(s)' or 'Str' and are usually listed after sailing vessels of the same name. Masters' names are given, arranged in approximate alphabetical order where there is more than one vessel of the same name. Latterly, details of tonnage and port of registry are often included.

Before 1908 index entries refer to issues of *Lloyd's List*, but do not give actual details of movements and casualties. The earliest entries (1838 to mid 1839) give only the date of issue, but thereafter the arrangement of the entries developed over the years, as indicated in the following examples:

1839—1847
   e.g. June $\frac{2}{3}$ indicates an entry in *Lloyd's List* of 2 June, column 3

1848—1907
e.g. June 2   indicates an arrival at or sailing from Liverpool (or casualty
    Liv 3   reported from that port), reported in *Lloyd's List* of 2 June,
          column 3

1908—1927
e.g. June 2/3 indicates an arrival (etc.) at Liverpool which occurred on 1 June
    Liv 1/6 and was reported in *Lloyd's List* of 2 June, column 3.

An index to abbreviations used in *Lloyd's List* indexes is being compiled and can be consulted at the Printed Books Enquiry Desk.

Several devices were used to distinguish arrivals from sailings, speakings and casualties. Between 1839 and 1848 separate columns were used. After 1848 'colour coding' was adopted: initially black for arrivals and red for other categories (with a 'd' over casualty entries), later black for arrivals, red for sailings and speakings and blue for 'paragraphs' (casualties etc.) However, these differentiations are not easily distinguished on the (black and white) microfilm.

After 1908 it is possible to trace movements in the index without reference to *Lloyd's List* itself, unless, of course, the obstacles of abbreviations and colour coding prove insurmountable. The 'Voyage Record Cards' (see Section 13) follow the same principle.

In the indexes from the 1890s onwards, and particularly for the First World War period, references with the prefix 'c.c.' are sometimes found. These refer to 'confidential circulars'.

A card index to news items is also available. It covers roughly the period 1920 to 1970, although it appears that in many cases cards from the earlier part of the period, presumably considered redundant, have been reversed and reused at a later date. The index should not, therefore, be considered comprehensive. General Subject Headings tend to be inconsistent and 48 hours' notice is required to consult them.

13. Voyage Record Cards

1927-c. 1975
(48 hours' notice required)

The contents of the earlier 'Voyage Record Cards' are arranged similarly to the later (post-1908) *Lloyd's List* indexes (see Section 12) and can be used in a similar way. The cards basically are a continuation of the *Lloyd's List* indexes. The date of change over was October 1927. Ships are distinguished by name, net tonnage and port of registry. Names of captains are given, together with dates of appointment. After 1947 cards were largely made up of cuttings from *Lloyd's Voyage Record* (see Section 15), with references to casualties entered in manuscript.

Troopships movements are not included on the cards, but such details can be gleaned from *Troopships that survived the War* (see below) or the manuscript notebooks 'Confidential Movements of Vessels on Special Government Service 1939-45' (see below, *Lloyd's Confidential Sheets*).

The movements of each vessel are recorded on one or more cards, arranged alphabetically by ship's name, but the filing of the cards is somewhat unusual, as it has been constantly under revision. Whenever the current file became unwieldy a new one was started, using the current card of each vessel that was still afloat. Consequently the cards of vessels which were no longer in service, together with the non-current cards of existing vessels were left behind as a 'dead' file. The process was repeated and by the time the collection was deposited there were about a dozen files, often with cards relating to a single vessel widely spread among them. At the time of writing the first six files (1927 c. 1946/7) have been interfiled and it is hoped that eventually the remainder will be added to make a single sequence.

An index to abbreviations used on the 'Voyage Record Cards' and in the *Lloyd's List* indexes is being compiled and can be consulted at the Printed Books Enquiry Desk.

14. Lloyd's Shipping Index

1880-April 1917, October 1917-March 1919, July 1927-June 1928, October 1928-March 1929, July 1929-March 1931, July 1931- June 1945, September 1945 to within 5 years.

Lloyd's Weekly Shipping Index, 1880-June 1914.
Lloyd s Weekly Index, July 1914-April 1917.
Lloyd's Confidential Daily List, October 1917-November 1918.
Lloyd's Daily Index, December 1918-May 1932. No April 1919 to June 1927 held at Guildhall Library.
Lloyd's Daily Shipping Index, May 1932-January 1936.
Lloyd's Shipping Index, February 1936 to within 5 years.

also *Vessels on Government Service* 1914-18,1939-45.

Lloyd's Weekly Shipping Index and *Lloyd's Weekly Index* reprinted much of the information which had appeared in *Lloyd's List* during the previous week, rearranged, in the case of the movements and casualties sections, into alphabetical order. Subsequently they were replaced by a daily index of shipping movements, the news and casualty sections being dropped. (The latter were replaced, from 1920, by *Lloyd's Weekly Casualty Reports*; see Section 16). Sample issues of these daily indexes were kept (one per week). Unfortunately a number of volumes are missing from the collection, notably those for the period April 1919 to June 1927, which were discarded many years ago.

The movements sections of *Lloyd's Shipping Index* have remained much the same since 1880. While sailing vessels continued in regular commercial use they were listed separately and in the 1930s a third, 'miscellaneous' category was introduced for movements of tugs etc. Vessels are identified by flag and tonnage, rig (sailing vessels only), owner or manager (1891 onwards, steamers and motor vessels only) and master (sailing vessels only). There is also an indication of the classification society responsible for classing each vessel. Details of the port and date of sailing and intended destination on a vessel's current voyage are given, together with the latest report available. The latter can include a reference to a casualty reported in detail elsewhere (indicated by the date on which the report appeared, prefixed by a Maltese cross).

During both World Wars separate indexes of the movements of *Vessels on Government Service* were published for restricted circulation. Those for the First World War are now available only on microfilm (in the Printed Books Reading Room). Those for the Second are bound similarly to *Lloyd's Shipping Index* and should be ordered in the normal way. The *Shipping Index* includes only the most recent information available at the time of printing and not necessarily all sailings and arrivals reported in *Lloyd's List*.

15. Lloyd's Voyage Record

1946 to within 5 years (not published August-November 1974).

Lloyd's Shipping Index: Voyage Supplement, 1946-April 1972.
Lloyd's Voyage Record, May 1972 to within 5 years.
Sept. 1975 to Dec. 1976 on microfiche only.

Published weekly, *Lloyd's Voyage Record* reprints the movements of ocean-going ships on their current voyages, in alphabetical order by ship, giving all reported dates of sailing and arrival; and is therefore much more comprehensive than *Lloyd's Shipping Index*. The later 'Voyage Record Cards' are based on this publication.

The V*oyage Record* is now published in both microfiche and hard copy. The fiche holds additional information i.e. each entry has at the top brief details of the vessel e.g. tonnage and owner manager. The first issue of the fiche was in 1976.

16. Lloyd's Weekly Casualty Reports

July 1920-December 1985.

Lloyd's Weekly Casualty Reports is in effect the continuation of the casualties section of *Lloyd's Weekly Shipping Index* (see Section 14). It is a weekly compilation of reports reprinted from *Lloyd's List* of the previous week, bound and indexed quarterly. Second copies of the indexes for the periods July 1920 to August 1939 and 1951 to 1970 have been collected into an envelope and six bound volumes.

17. Lloyd's List Weekly Summary

1880-1920.

Mitchell's Maritime Register, 1880-83. January to June 1881 on microfilm.
Shipping Gazette and Lloyd's List Weekly Summary, 1884-June 1914. 1899 No index.
Shipping Gazette Weekly Summary, July 1914-January 1916.
Lloyd's List Weekly Summary, February 1916-1920.

Mitchell's Maritime Register was first published in 1856, but the volumes for 1880 are the earliest available in the Library. Following the publication's change of name in 1884 its history closely follows that of *Lloyd's List* (see Section 11). Publication continued until 1934, although our file ends in 1920.

The *Weekly Summary* includes reports of shipping movements and casualties, leading articles, law and official inquiry reports and news items, most of which may also be found in *Lloyd's List*. However, unlike *Lloyd's List*, until 1915 the volumes include annual indexes to law cases, leading articles, official inquiries and (from 1904) company reports and meetings. The *Weekly Summary* is particularly useful as a source for Board of Trade inquiry reports in the period before the beginning of our holdings of the official series (1908).

Note: only the volumes for 1916-20 are, strictly speaking, part of the Lloyd's Marine Collection, the earlier volumes being part of Guildhall Library's own collections.

18. Lloyd's List Supplementary Mail Advices

July 1926-May 1941, Mar 1947-1965.

Duplicated typescript sheets produced daily to supplement reports of shipping movements published in *Lloyd's List*. They are based on the written reports of Lloyd's agents and do not include movements which had previously been telegraphed. They are arranged by port and are indexed by the 'Voyage Record Cards', in which the entries can be distinguished by the capital letters (relating to a sheet) which replace the column number. This publication was discontinued after May 17 1941 and did not resume until after the War.

19. Lloyd's Confidential Sheets

September 1939-December 1945.

Lloyd's *Confidential Sheets* were produced daily (in duplicated typescript). They are bound and indexed quarterly or half-yearly. The information given comprises reports of movements and casualties of vessels on Government service, including many which do not appear in *Vessels on Government Service* or *Lloyd's Weekly*

Casualty Reports. Only the casualties are covered by the indexes, but references to both movements and casualties are included in the 'Voyage Record Cards'. References are differentiated in the same way as the *Supplementary Mail Advices*, by the substitution of a capital letter (relating to a sheet) for the column number.

Complementing the *Confidential Sheets* are a small number of manuscript notebooks, 'Confidential Movements of Vessels on Special Government Service 1939-45'. Compiled by staff at Lloyd's they are arranged chronologically and alphabetically by ship within each notebook. They list the movements of a variety of vessels and hospital ships and include many vessels from the U.S.A.

20. Ministry of Transport

Troopships that survived the War.

Extracted from Ministry of Transport records now at the Public Record Office, Kew, classed as MT 40, these photostat sheets are an alphabetical list of troopships on Government service throughout the Second World War. The details for each entry include vessel's owners prior to Government takeover, technical details of the ship, troop carrying capacity and details of voyages. The latter include not just dates of arrival and sailing from various ports but notes on repairs undertaken and date of release from troop transport duties. There are no entries for troopships lost during the war.

21. Yacht and Whaler Movements

October 1946-1968 (with some loose parts to 1973).

Yacht Movements, 1946-54.
Yacht and Whaler Movements, 1955-73.

Duplicated typewritten sheets produced daily. They are arranged by port. After 1955 yacht and whaler movements are grouped in separate sequences, bound together. The yacht movements are indexed between 1955 and 1961 by a series of manuscript volumes similar to the original *Lloyd's List* indexes. These volumes index yacht movements reported in *Yacht and Whaler Movements* and casualties reported in *Lloyd's List*. Their spines are titled simply 'Yachts'.

22. Shipping and Mercantile Gazette

1864-June 1884.

Earlier issues of the publication which was amalgamated with *Lloyd's List* in July 1884. They are included here for the sake of completeness.

23. Board of Trade

Wreck Registers U.K. 1855-1898.

These microfilms have been made from records held at the National Maritime Museum. They hold information which has come from the Registrar at each port about loss of vessels. What has been included is only those vessels registered at a British port. The origin of the records lies in the Merchant Shipping Act 1854.

The information contained includes name of vessel, port of registry, official number, name of master, number of his certificate, name and address of owners or agents, brief report of the casualty, authority for the report, any references to correspondence and the result and any wages paid to the master.

Not to be confused with the scrap book entitled Wreck Register. The reports are listed alphabetically from 1855 to 1859, 1863 to 1864 and 1873 to 1898 and chronologically from 1860 to 1862 and 1864 to 1873. Apart from part of 1863, each volume of the chronological lists has its own index.

24. Board of Trade Casualty Returns

1850-1918 (1850 to 1878/9 in Parliamentary Papers only. 1879/80-1918 is a separate and additional set in the Lloyd's Marine Collection).

Abstracts of the Returns made to the Board of Trade of Sea Casualties . . ., 1850-1883/4.
Abstracts of the Returns made to the Board of Trade of Shipping Casualties..., 1884/5-1911/12.
Return of Shipping Casualties and Loss of Life, 1912/13-1914/18.

also *Merchant Ships Foundered and Missing 1st July 1873 to 16th May 1880,* (C.2625, 1880). In Parl. Papers 1880 vol. 66.
Merchant Ships Foundered and Missing 1st January 1880 to 31st December 1883, (C.4628, 1887).
Sea Casualties (Wreck Statistics 1875-86), (C.5364, 1888).

The Board of Trade returns relate to British vessels lost anywhere in the world and foreign vessels lost on the coasts of the United Kingdom and British possessions abroad. They were made to Parliament and are therefore also available in Guildhall Library's set of Parliamentary Papers. Up to and including the issue covering 1914/18 (published 1921) they comprised extensive statistics of shipping casualties and loss of life at sea, together with details of each vessel lost. Subsequently the specific cases were omitted and Lloyd's ceased to file the series. The returns normally give the name of each vessel, its age, rig or type, tonnage, number of crew, cargo, date, place and type of casualty (i.e. wreck or collision) wind force and direction and number of lives lost. From 1864, information on the voyage (Port sailed from and to) was added; and from 1872 the names of the master and ship owner. A separate leaflet identifying the relevant volumes of Parliamentary Papers for the Board of Trade casualty returns is available.

Three other Parliamentary returns are shelved with this series, one, *Sea Casualties (Wreck Statistics 1875-86)*, purely statistical, the others, two volumes of *Merchant Ships Foundered and Missing*, giving details of losses falling into these two categories during the period 1873-83. The information given is similar to that appearing in the later annual returns, but includes details of the outcome of any official inquiries held.

25. Bureau Veritas Publications

1896-1938.

Annual Summary of Wrecks and Casualties, 1896-1922.
Monthly List of Wrecks and Casualties, 1923-34.
Statistiques Mensuelles, Nouvelles Entrées, Radiations, Liste des Pertes et Accidents, 1935-8.
These series, published by the French equivalent of Lloyd's Register of Shipping, Bureau Veritas, are international in coverage. They give statistics and brief details of vessels lost and damaged, arranged in separate sequences for steamers, sailing vessels and, latterly, motor vessels. Particulars of launches, new construction and name changes were included from 1935 onwards. The publications were bilingual until 1934, but subsequently appeared in French only.

Note: the spines of these volumes are labelled 'V losses' and this title may be used in ordering them.

26. Liverpool Underwriters' Casualty Returns

March 1934-July 1939, 1946-80.

Offprints from *Lloyd's List* of monthly returns, made by the Liverpool Underwriters' Association, of casualties to steam and motor vessels of 500 tons (gross) and over. They comprise statistics and details of the 'more important' casualties (including cargo and particulars of the incident).

27. Lloyd's Total Loss Returns

December 1947-January 1969.

Also known as 'Marine Total Losses', having no formal title. The volumes consist of duplicated typescript sheets, arranged monthly with British and foreign vessels grouped in separate sequences. The volumes for the period December 1947 to May 1954 are indexed. The layout is similar to that of Lloyd's Second

World War loss books, as is the information given (see Section 30). This includes brief details of voyage and cargo and a 'report' showing the position and circumstances of the loss.

28. Marine Loss Cards

1939-90.

also 'Missing Vessels Cards', c.1939-c.1970.
(48 hours' notice required)

The 'Marine Loss Cards' form an index to merchant shipping losses during the period 1939 to 1972. The term Marine Loss refers to vessels lost by causes other than war. The earlier cards are similar to the "War Loss Cards" (see Section 31) and contain brief information on circumstances and position of loss, voyage, cargo and number of lives lost. The later cards (c.1950 onwards) comprise cuttings from *Lloyd's List*. Occasionally the initials of the insurance brokers involved appear on the cards.

The 'Missing Vessels Cards' cover vessels which were reported overdue and/or posted missing during roughly the same period. Their layout is similar to that of the 'Marine Loss Cards'. They complement the 'Missing Vessels Books' (see Section 35), which cover the period 1873 to 1954, although whereas the latter include only vessels that had been formally 'posted missing' at Lloyd's, the cards appear to include references to all vessels reported overdue, whatever the final outcome.

29. Board of Trade Inquiry Reports

1908-65.

Reports of Board of Trade inquiries into wrecks and casualties, published by HMSO. This file begins with no. 7126 (1908). The later volumes include press cuttings (and occasionally other documents) relating to some of the cases. Each volume covers two or more years and is indexed. Two additional volumes contain correspondence from the period January 1924 to April 1947 (mainly standard letters from the Board of Trade announcing forthcoming inquiries) and second copies of inquiry reports for the period 1924 to c.1940.

Summary reports for the period 1880 to 1915 may be found in *Mitchell's Maritime Register* and *Shipping Gazette Weekly Summary* (see under heading *Lloyd's List Weekly Summary,* Section 17) which have annual indexes.

Inquiry reports were not published prior to 1876. Precis reports 1856-76 were included in the casualty returns, copies of which are held by the Department of Trade Marine Library, and are included in Parliamentary Papers. See separate leaflet on Board of Trade casualty returns.

It is worth noting that although a preliminary inquiry is held into every British casualty only certain incidents receive full formal inquiries. Reports of preliminary inquiries were not published.

Other supplementary sources are *The Times* (indexed under wrecks) and *The Illustrated London News* for which there is a card index 1842 to 1875.

30. Lloyd's War Loss Books

'Casualties to Shipping through Enemy Causes, 1914-1918 (Lloyd's Official List)', 2 vols. (Ms 14, 934A/1-2), published in a one volume facsimile reprint as *Lloyd's War Losses: the First World War* (1990).

'Lloyd's War Losses: the Second World War', 3 vols in 5, published in facsimile reprint as *Lloyd's War Losses: the Second World War*. Vols 1-3 (1989-93).

See also 'War Casualty Books' (under 'Lloyd's Loss and Casualty Books', Section 34).

For reasons of conservation and convenience readers are asked to use the facsimile reprints of the originals published by Lloyd's of London Press. They are to be found in the Printed Books Reading Room.

Lloyd's First World War Loss Book lists only British, Allied and Neutral casualties. The main sequence is a chronological list of vessels destroyed by submarines, mines, cruisers or aircraft. There are also a number of shorter lists of vessels damaged by the same causes, sunk or damaged during bombardment, detained, captured and missing or untraced and a supplementary list of vessels sunk by mines between the end of the War and 1925. The facsimile edition has an Index which refers to all sections of the Loss Book.

Each entry gives the name, flag and tonnage of the vessel, the cause of her loss or damage (where appropriate), the place where she was lost, the voyage she was on and a brief description (usually one word) of her cargo. Details of locations can vary between a precise bearing and no more than a general expression such as 'Bay of Biscay' or 'Channel'. Lloyd's War Losses can be considered an improvement on the Admiralty Lists, *Merchant Shipping (losses)* (House of Commons Paper 199, 1919). This is because the Admiralty Lists do not give details about voyage or cargo for either British or foreign vessels and there are a number of errors and omissions.

Lloyd's Second World War Loss Books record losses and casualties of both Allied and enemy vessels. In facsimile, Vol. 1 is a chronological record of British, Allied and Neutral merchant vessels sunk or destroyed by war causes. There follows a list of British, Allied and Neutral Vessels captured by the enemy, excluding vessels registered in overrun territory. War loss as a definition refers strictly and directly to loss by bomb, torpedoes or mines.

Volume 2 continues with a statistical analysis of the contents of Vol. 1. There then follows a section on vessels posted at Lloyd's as missing or untraced. The arrangement is once again chronological and the date in question refers to the date the vessel was officially considered as lost. Next comes Allied vessels seriously damaged by war causes, Allied naval vessels lost, Allied vessels lost to mines since hostilities (up to 1957), those damaged by mines since hostilities and an index to all entries other than in the last section which has its own index.

The third volume is devoted to enemy casualties and contains two alphabetical lists, one of German, Italian and other Axis vessels and the other of Japanese vessels. Please note that at the time of writing, the third volume has not yet appeared in facsimile.

Each entry includes the name, flag and tonnage of the vessel and the position and cause of her loss. Voyage and cargo details of British, Allied and Neutral vessels are sometimes given, together with the number of lives lost. Additional information often appears in a 'remarks' column.

31. War Loss Cards

1939-c. 1975.
(48 hours' notice required)

Lloyd's 'War Loss Cards' formed a day-to-day record of shipping lost or damaged as a result of enemy action during the Second World War. The information was subsequently used to compile Lloyd's Second World War Loss Books (see Section 30). The details on the cards are similar to those in the books, comprising name, tonnage, owner and flag of vessel, the position and cause of the incident, a brief description of the cargo and numbers of personnel lost and saved. Sometimes additional material is included; for example, variant reports of position or cause or fuller particulars of the cargo reported in connection with later salvage attempts. As in the books, details of post-War losses due to war causes (usually mines) are included.

The file is divided into three sequences: British, Allied and Neutral; 'Enemy' (i.e. German and other Axis); and Japanese.

References to German, other Axis and Japanese vessels will include only those sunk during the period of actual hostilities.

32. Other Sources of Information on War Losses

When the Lloyd's Marine Collection came to Guildhall Library it was accompanied by a number of miscellaneous items relating to shipping losses during the two World Wars. While these are still in the Collection, they have been augmented by other sources mostly published more recently and thus containing new or more accurate information. Some of the items described below therefore are not part of the Collection, but their importance is such that they are considered worthy of inclusion. The section is divided into parts for the First and Second World Wars and only includes material not previously mentioned.

First World War

Lloyd's Prizes of War. (1917).
This work includes war casualties and vessels and cargoes detained. There are eight sections — German vessels; Austrian; Turkish; British; Allied; Neutral vessels whose cargoes or part of them have been detained and finally Unclassified. Within each section there are sub sections listing different categories relevant to that nation's vessels. In other words the first section, for example, which is devoted to German vessels is broken down into those ships 'Detained in oversea British ports, Detained in other countries ports (separately listed), Sunk, Captured' etc. This format is repeated in the other main sections.
The Library copy has pencilled additions providing more information. Each sub section is divided alphabetically. There is a single sequence alphabetical index.
The comprehensive coverage of the work, including as it does vessels for the Central Powers (Germany, Austria and Turkey) makes it a valuable supplement to Lloyd's War Losses: the First World War, although *Prizes of War* finishes its coverage in 1917.

Lloyd's. 'Return of ships sunk during the Great War'. (1918).
This item has been produced by binding into four volumes photocopies of frail original sheets. It gives particulars of vessels sunk around the U.K., French and Spanish coasts and in the North Sea during the War. What is shown is position, date, voyage, nature of cargo and insurance or reinsurance values so far as is known. The order is chronological.

Board of Trade. *Government War Risks Insurance Scheme. List of Vessels Lost, Damaged or Missing. (1918-1920). Part One 1 August 1914-31 December 1917. Part Two 1 January 1918-31 May 1920.*
This is a printed but unpublished list. Information shown includes insured value of vessels other than those on Government Service and particulars of the loss, including numbers of personnel killed, injured or taken prisoner.
Guildhall Library only had Part Two originally as part of the Lloyd's Marine Collection. Part One was more recently acquired through the good offices of the Department of Transport Domestic Shipping Policy Emergencies Division.

Ministry of Shipping. Shipping Intelligence Section. *Service List. World War One.* (1921). 2 vols.
The volumes comprise a list of vessels engaged for naval, military and commercial purposes with dates of entry and discharge, rates of hire etc. Where a vessel has been lost this information has been given. The order is chronological with brief technical details about each vessel and then the record of its use. Very useful indications on cargo, troops carried etc.

Spindler, Arno. *Der Handelskrieg mit U Booten.* (1932-4). 5 vols.
This is a thorough survey of the German U Boat campaign against British and Allied shipping from the outbreak of war to 1918. The last two volumes of the German edition contain indexes. The Admiralty in London commissioned a translation of the first three volumes (which were the only ones available at the time) covering the years 1914 to January 1918. The translation was entitled *The submarine war against commerce.*

Tennent, A. J. *British merchant ships sunk by U Boats in the 1914-1918 war.* (1990).

This is a simple and straightforward guide to British vessels lost between 1914-1918. The arrangement is alphabetical, first by shipping company and then by ship's name. Entries include ship's former name if appropriate, gross registered tonnage, year built, date of loss, how sunk, position and direction of voyage and number of crew lost. There is an index of ships' names, also a place index.

First World War Boxes.

There are a number of items in the boxes that are duplicates of documents elsewhere in the Collection. However there are three sources, one copy only of each in the Collection, which merit a note:

Blom and Van Der Aa. *List of steamers and sailing vessels lost or damaged in consequence of the war, up to March 31st 1916.*

This is an alphabetical list of vessels of all nationalities, published by a Dutch firm of insurance brokers and underwriters.

Losses in Portuguese waters, 1916-1917.

This is an extract from an unidentified Portuguese publication.

Lloyd's lists of German steamers and sailing vessels and Austro-Hungarian, Turkish and Bulgarian steamers (1000 tons and over), showing 'latest report at Lloyd's'.

Printed lists covering the period 1914-1918, shelved with, but not in First World War Boxes.

The boxes also contain three Admiralty Lists:

Merchant Shipping (Losses) (House of Commons Paper 199, 1919).

Foreign Vessels sunk or damaged by the Enemy from the outbreak of war to 11th November 1918. (Printed 'for official use only', 1919).

Navy Losses (House of Commons Paper 200, 1919).

There are duplicates of the Admiralty lists elsewhere, separately catalogued.

Second World War.

Orde, G. P. *Dunkirk withdrawal, Operation Dynamo, May 26 to June 1940: alphabetical list of vessels taking part with their services.* (1940). 3 vols. in 6 parts.

Using official papers, some of which no longer exist, this document appears to be the only definitive list of all vessels which took part in Operation Dynamo. Each entry shows the name or number of the craft, the person in command of it, dates, times and notes on what the vessel was doing. There are a few references to personnel usually because of death, injury or awards made for gallantry.

Rohwer, J. *Die U Boot erfolge der Achsenmachte 1939-1945./Axis submarine successes 1939-1945.* (1983). Introductory material translated by John A Broadwin.

Originally published in German in 1968, this translation is the product of research on declassified records since the German edition appeared. The United States Naval Institute organised and published the English language version. Despite the revised information contained in it naval experts still consider it to contain errors. This has to be borne in mind when consulting it.

The book is broken up into seven areas of Axis submarine activity: North Sea – Atlantic; Northern Theatre; Baltic; Black Sea; Mediterranean; Indian Ocean and Pacific Ocean. Within each theatre the entries are arranged chronologically and by fifteen columns across the page, i.e. date of attack, submarine nationality, position etc. There are four indexes – U Boats, U Boat captains, Convoys and Ships Attacked.

Ministry of War Transport. *Small craft service list (1st June 1944), British and foreign merchant ships and miscellaneous craft in service of H.M. Government since 3rd September 1939.* (1946).
Ministry of War Transport. *Service list. British and foreign merchant ships etc . . . in service of H.M. Government since 3rd September 1939 to 1st September 1946.* (1946).
These two works cover merchant vessels from Britain and abroad and miscellaneous craft irrespective of tonnage, owned, chartered or requisitioned by the Government during the War. Includes details of owners/previous owners, terms of employment, nature of service and where appropriate rates of hire.
The *Small Craft Service List* includes those vessels under three hundred gross registered tons and the *Service List* those over three hundred gross registered tons.

Admiralty Lists.
As with the First World War there are three lists produced by the Admiralty concerning the Second World War. They may be consulted although their publication so soon after the War makes them prone to errors and omissions.
British Merchant Vessels Lost or Damaged by Enemy action during Second World War (1947).
Ships of the Royal Navy: statement of losses during the Second World War (1947).
British and Foreign Merchant Vessels Lost or Damaged by Enemy Action during Second World War (B.R. 1337 (Restricted), 1945). Printed 'for official use only'. Includes manuscript alterations and amendments. Also printed lists of amendments.

Second World War Boxes
There are two boxes containing documents, some of which are duplicate copies, i.e. two of the Admiralty Lists mentioned above. However also included are single copies of:

U.S.A. Navy Department. *Japanese Naval and Merchant Shipping Losses during World War Two by all causes* (1947). Chronological list with alphabetical index. Also alphabetical list of U.S. submarines and their victims.

List of Finnish Merchant Vessels lost during the 1939-1945 War.
Norske Veritas. *Norges, Sveriges og Danmarke handelsflåter, tilgang og avgang i 1940-1945.* Statistics and details of Norwegian, Swedish and Danish merchant shipping losses (war and marine).

Sjøfartskontoret. *Krigsforliste Norske skip, 3 September 1939 – 8 Mai 1945.* Statistics and details of Norwegian war losses, with manuscript annotations and amendments.

Sjøfartskonoret. *Norsk sjøulykkestatistikk for 1939-45.* Statistics and details of Norwegian marine losses during the War.

33. Lloyd's Subscription Books

1774-6, 1785-6, 1789-95, 1797-1806, 1809, 1811-24, 1826-44, November-December 1847, November-December 1849 (86 vols, Ms. 14,931/1-86).

Cover title:
'New Lloyd's Coffee House Subscribers' Book', 1774-89.
'Lloyd's Subscription Room', 1789-1801.
No title, 1802-49.

The 'Subscription Books' may be consulted in the Manuscripts Section where a detailed catalogue is available. They were deposited at Guildhall Library in 1974, five years before the deposit of the remainder of the Collection.

Volumes containing reports of arrivals and casualties (usually undated), entered daily, as received, and intended for the benefit of subscribers who visited Lloyd's. In the case of arrivals, information is confined to name of vessel, name of master and ports of sailing and arrival. Arrivals of the mails are also recorded. The casualty reports are very similar in wording to those that were published in *Lloyd's List.* After 1837 they can also be found in Lloyd's 'Loss Books' (see Section 34).

It seems that many of the entries which appeared in *Lloyd's List* were not previously recorded in the 'Subscription Books'. *Lloyd's List* is, therefore, the more complete of the two sources and the 'Subscription Books', which are unindexed, are little used.

34. Lloyd's Loss and Casualty Books

1837-19 December 1847, 1848-31 December 1982 (125 vols, Ms 14,932/1-125). Index volumes July 1852-25 September 1854, 29 October 1855-1876,1878-1934, 1936-31 December 1982 (114 vols, Ms 14,933/1-114).
'Loss Books', 1837-1913.
'Casualty Books', 1914-82

also 'War Casualty Books', 5 August 1914-16 June 1922 (4 vols. Ms 14,934/1-4) and index volumes thereto April 1917-16 June 1922 (2 vols, Ms 14,935/1-2).

The 'Loss and Casualty Books' may be consulted in the Manuscripts Section, where a detailed catalogue is available. Like the 'Subscription Books' they were deposited at Guildhall Library in 1974.

Volumes containing reports of casualties, entered daily as received. The early entries duplicate the reports of casualties in the 'Subscription Books'. After 1850 the entries were expanded to include the type of vessel, a brief description of the cargo and the source of information. In general they correspond to the initial reports which appeared in *Lloyd's List*, but the latter often includes additional reports and can therefore offer more information.

The early volumes of the 'Loss and Casualty Books' (apart from volumes 4 and 5, which duplicate part of volume 3 anyway) include indexes. The indexes for July 1852 onwards form a separate series of volumes. They are arranged according to the initial letters of vessels' names, but entries under each letter of the alphabet were added chronologically.

The 'Casualty Books' are still compiled and the current volume, together with the one for a hundred years previously, is displayed in 'the Room' at Lloyd's. The latter is not, therefore, available at Guildhall Library during the year in which it is on display. Under the 1982 alteration of the terms of deposit (see Introduction) the volumes returned to the Library after being displayed become the property of the Library.

In addition to the main series of 'Casualty Books' there are four volumes of 'War Casualty Books', in which are recorded details of merchant vessels lost or damaged through war causes during and immediately following the First World War. The entries were made daily in the same way as those in the 'Casualty Books'. (The latter are largely confined to marine losses, although some war losses appear in both series.) There are two indexes to the 'War Casualty Books', covering the period 1 April 1917 to 16 June 1922. These 'War Casualty Books' are complemented by the 'official' First World War Loss Books (Ms 14,934A), compiled after the War, which are described in Section 30, and available in facsimile reprint.

35. Lloyd's Missing Vessels Books

1873-1954.

also 'Vessels against which closing entries have been made in the Daily Index', 1916-January 1946.

See also 'Missing Vessels Cards' (under 'Marine Loss Cards', Section 28).

In 1866 the Committee of Lloyd's resolved to keep a book in which all vessels 'posted missing' by the Committee were to be recorded. This was done in order that insurance claims might be settled. The earliest to survive is the volume covering the period 1873 to 1875, beginning with entry no. 765. Each entry gives particulars of the vessel and the voyage she was on at the time of her disappearance, a brief description of her cargo and sometimes the names of the insurers, as well as details of the application to have her posted missing. Some entries include cuttings from *Lloyd's List* or other additional material. Each volume is indexed by ship's name.

Not all vessels which disappeared without trace were posted missing. Those that were not, probably because there was no insurance interest on the market, were entered in a register of 'Vessels against which closing entries have been made in the Daily Index'. Some volumes, covering roughly the periods of the two World Wars, have survived in the Lloyd's Marine Collection. Entries are much the same as those in 'Lloyd's Missing Vessels Books', though without details of insurers.

Note: 'Lloyd's Missing Vessels Books' are arranged chronologically and bound into volumes covering irregular numbers of years. The year required should therefore be stated on the request slip.

36. Lloyd's Captains Registers

1869 (but including some retrospective details)-1948 (143 vols and 11 boxes of cards, Mss 18,567/1-87, 18,568/1-15, 18,569/1-41, 18,570/1-9, 18,571/1-2).

The 'Captains Registers' may be consulted in the Manuscripts Section, where a detailed catalogue is available.

Voluntary examinations of competency for prospective masters and mates of foreign-going British merchant vessels were introduced in 1845, authorised by the Board of Trade. They were made compulsory by the Mercantile Marine Act of 1850 (taking effect in 1851) and extended to the home trade under the Merchant Shipping Act 1854. When compulsory examinations were introduced provision was made for Certificates of Service, in the appropriate capacity, to be issued without examination to men who had served as masters or mates of British merchant vessels before 1 January 1851 and to officers of the Royal Navy and the East India Company. (See Part Two, Section 2.1 for information on surviving official records.)

Lloyd's 'Captains Registers' form a record of the service as captain or mate of holders of British master's certificates between the years 1869 and 1948 (with some earlier details) based on information supplied to Lloyd's by the Registrar General of Shipping and Seamen. The majority of the entries refer to men who had obtained their certificates in the United Kingdom, although there are some references to men with certificates issued at ports in British possessions overseas. The 'Captains Registers' do not ordinarily contain information about masters of coasters, fishing vessels, ferries or yachts. However an exception to that is the initials HT written above the certificate number meaning Home Trade. This refers to non ocean-going vessels.

The first *Lloyd's Captains Register* was published in 1869 and listed holders of master's certificates who were active at that date. Names and, where appropriate, official numbers of the vessels on which they had served since obtaining their certificates are given, the earliest entries dating from 1851 when the holding of a certificate first became compulsory. In most cases the latest entry is for 1868, although sometimes it is earlier. However, no one who was known, at the time of compilation, to have died or retired before 1868 is included. A copy of this volume may be consulted at the Printed Books Enquiry Desk.

New entries in the 'Captains Registers' were initially published in *Lloyd's List*, but these are not indexed. No further registers were published in volume form. However, a copy of the 1869 publication was cut up and the individual entries pasted into large volumes in which the record was continued in manuscript. There are six series of these manuscript volumes (Ms 18,567/1-87), the first covering c.1851-73 (including the printed entries), the second 1874-9 and the remainder the four eight-year periods between 1880 and 1911. Entries are arranged roughly alphabetically by surname, with new additions at the bottom of each page or in extra folios at the end of each alphabetical section. In the latter case there are usually references from the appropriate places in the main sequence.

In 1912 a new system was adopted and engagements were recorded on typescript sheets, one or, if necessary, more for each captain. A retrospective record of the career of each captain included in the new-style registers was compiled from the manuscript volumes.

There are two series of these typescript sheets. The first (Ms 18,568/1-15) covers the period up to 1948, the majority of entries referring to captains who were still active at that date. The second (Ms 18,569/1-41) appears to comprise sheets extracted from the first because they were no longer current, the captains to which they refer having died or retired before the registers ceased to be compiled (i.e. before 1948). However, on most sheets in the first series (Ms 18,568/1-15) the last entries date from 1947 or even earlier.

In addition there are two card indexes of holders of master's certificates who did not actually serve as captains. One (Ms 18,570/1-9) is of men who served only as mates, 1912-48, and the other (Ms 18,571/1-2) is of men who were not known to have taken up any appointment by 1948.

Each entry in the 'Captains Registers' includes the subject's name and the place and year of his birth, together with the place and year of his examination (when applicable) and the number of his certificate. In the early volumes the numbers of certificates of service (based on experience) are prefixed with an 'S' and those of competence (based on examination) with a 'C'. Any restrictive qualifications (e.g. a 'steam' certificate) or awards are also noted and dates of death are sometimes given. The 'crown' symbol against some entries indicates membership of the Royal Naval Reserve. The restrictive nature of some certificates refers to the fact that some masters were not entitled to command certain types of vessels. One such indication in the Registers is the phrase 'fore and aft' i.e. not qualified to command square rigged vessels. Also the initials HT already mentioned above. There were special qualifications too, such as an 'Extra' certificate indicating advanced levels of seamanship.

The record of each master's service includes the name and official number of each vessel on which he served either as captain or mate after obtaining his master's certificate. The first, printed, register gives the years in which he served on each ship, while the manuscript and typescript registers give precise dates of engagement and in some cases discharge. An indication of the destination, in general terms of each intended voyage (shown by an abbreviated 'code' to which a key is available at the Manuscripts Enquiry Desk) is given after the name of each ship. Any casualties that may have occurred are recorded, usually with a reference to a report in *Lloyd's List* and the number of any Board of Trade Inquiry that may have resulted. It was not unusual for a qualified master mariner to serve as mate after receiving his master's certificate and this type of service is also recorded in the 'Captains Registers'. The printed register uses Roman type for the names of vessels on which a man served as master and italics for those on which he served as mate. Up to 1893 the manuscript volumes distinguish between appointments as master or as mate by underlining the names of those ships on which the man served as mate. After this date the name of the ship was written in black if he was master, or red if he was mate and in red underlined if he was serving as second or third mate.

Some masters and mates were subject to Marine Investigation Board Inquiries. The decisions of the Board were made known in 'Confidential Circulars'. A small number of these are in the Lloyd's Marine Collection. They range in date from 1900 to 1946. A note relating to these decisions is included in the 'Captains Registers' with a reference to the appropriate page number. Look for a number circled in blue. However it is emphasised only a small number survive in the Collection. The 'Circulars' are kept in the Manuscripts Section.

37. Lloyd's Confidential Index

1886 (sailing vessels 1894)-1920, British vessels only; 1921 onwards (30-year embargo), British and foreign vessels.

Lloyd's Confidential Index of British Steamships of 100 tons register and upwards, no. 1, July 1886-June 1920.

Lloyd's Confidential Index of British Sailing Vessels of 500 tons register and upwards, March 1894-July 1907.

Lloyd's Confidential Index of Sailing Vessels of United Kingdom registry, 500 tons register and upwards, January 1908-December 1915.

Lloyd's Confidential Index: Sailing Vessels of United Kingdom and Colonial Registry and Steamships of Colonial Registry, 500 tons net register and upwards, June 1915-December 1919.

Lloyd's Confidential Index of British Steam and Motor Vessels (of 500 tons gross register and upwards), December 1920 onwards.

Lloyd's Confidential Index of Foreign Steam and Motor Vessels (of 1000 tons gross register and upwards), July 1921 onwards.

Also *Return of British Steamship Owners showing the History of their Steamers of 100 tons register and over between the 1st July, 1880, and 1st July, 1885.* Not indexed by ship.

Lloyd's Confidential Index is published, as stated on the front covers of early issues, 'for the use of underwriters solely'. An embargo of thirty years has been placed on it. It was originally published three times a year (March, July and November), but since 1899 has been six-monthly. The issues in the Collection come from the records of Lloyd's Confidential Index (formerly a department of Lloyd's and now part of Lloyd's of London Press Ltd.) and all but the early issues (steam 1886-1904; sail 1894-1907, except March 1897, March 1899, January 1901 and January 1906) are annotated. The annotations comprise additions and amendments to the printed entries. After 1920, *Lloyd's Confidential Index* survives only on microfilm (kept in the cabinets in the Printed Books Reading Room).

Lloyd's Confidential Index is an alphabetical list of managing owners, giving details of the vessels in each fleet, including names, details of masters (up to 1920), voyages during the year prior to publication ('class of voyage' only after 1920), damage and alterations and particulars of vessels totally lost. Between 1890 and 1920 it included the names of holders of ten or more shares. Information on vessels sold or otherwise transferred is also included. There is an alphabetical index to vessels in each issue. The volumes for steam include damage repairs from 1885, and fleet additions from 1st January 1894.

Up to 1919 *Lloyd's Confidential Index* included an appendix listing masters whose certificates had been suspended, showing the reasons for suspension and details of their subsequent careers. These lists are cumulative, beginning in 1883, but appear to include only men who were active at the time of publication. They are indexed by the names of the vessels on which the men served, both at the time of suspension and afterwards.

38. Other Records of Lloyd's Confidential Index

In 1981 Lloyd's Confidential Index deposited microfilms of the department's records to supplement the original Lloyd's Marine Collection. These include the later issues of *Lloyd's Confidential Index*, described in the previous section, together with certain other records. The following are available for consultation by the public and will be found in the cabinets in the Printed Books Reading Room.

'Cemetery' cards
Lloyd's Confidential Index maintained card files on all vessels listed in *Lloyd's Confidential Index*, recording such details as changes of name or ownership and sometimes general descriptions of voyages. Whenever a vessel was removed, usually because it had been lost or broken up, its card was placed in the 'cemetery' files, of which there are two, covering, respectively, British and foreign vessels. Details of the reason for removal are usually given, though often confined to an abbreviated 'T/L' (total loss), 'B/U' (broken up) etc. The 'cemetery' files begin in about 1920.

Second World War Loss Cards
These are very similar to Lloyd's War Loss Cards, already described, although arranged differently (British and foreign as distinct from Allied, Enemy and Japanese). They include only vessels which appeared in *Lloyd's Confidenial Index*.

Spanish Civil War and Sino-Japanese War Loss Cards
One reel of microfilm covers both of these small files, which list vessels damaged, lost, seized or detained during the two wars. The section on the Spanish Civil War (1936-9) is arranged in three sequences, British, foreign/neutral and Spanish vessels, while that on the Sino-Japanese War (1937-9), erroneously headed 'Sino-Chinese War', is in a single sequence.

39. Lloyd's Calendar

1892-4, 1896-1985.

Lloyd's Seaman's Almanac, 1893-7.
Lloyd's Calendar, 1898-1980.
Lloyd's Nautical Yearbook, 1980-1985.

As its earlier title suggests, *Lloyd's Calendar* is primarily a seaman's almanac. It includes lists of recipients of Lloyd's Medals, some of them cumulative. The details are as follows:
Lloyd's Medal for Services to Lloyd's (instituted 1913); cumulative lists 1918-75,
Lloyd's Medal for Saving Life at Sea (instituted 1836); last cumulative list 1940.
Lloyd's Medal for Meritorious Service (instituted 1893); last cumulative list 1940,
Lloyd's War Medal for Bravery at Sea (instituted 1940); cumulative lists 1953-5
Plaques awarded to vessels 'instrumental in effecting rescues and whose boats' crews received Lloyd's Medals'; last cumulative list 1940.

Lloyd's medals are better researched by the use of J. Gawler's *Lloyd's Medals 1836-1989* (1989). This gives a full history of medals awarded by Lloyd's and gives details of a cross section of awards. There is a full index to all medals awarded by Lloyd's up to 1989 and there are citations for a selected number.

In addition citations for all Lloyd's War Medals for Bravery at Sea were published in special supplements in *Lloyd's List*. A set of these has been collected together as Lloyd's Books Fo. Pam. 27.

Citations for medals not included in these three sources may be obtained from the Manager's Secretarial Department, Lloyd's, Lime Street, London EC3M 7HL.

40. Sample Volumes

A small number of volumes remain in the Collection as examples of titles that have not been retained. Their practical usefulness is, of course, very limited. They are as follows:

Lloyd's List Indexes
Although the series of indexes to *Lloyd's List* is now only available for consulta-

tion on microfilm (see Section 12), five of the original volumes survive: 1850, N-S; 1852, A-D; 1896, D-E; 1912, T-Z; 1927, P-Z. They may not normally be consulted by the public.

Salvage Association reports and slips
The following two volumes survive: *London and Liverpool reports from 2nd July, 1866, to 29th June, 1867* (nos. 154 to 295) and *Slips from 2nd July, 1867, to 29th June, 1868* (nos. 590 to New Series 38). Each series comprises daily printed sheets of reports from Salvage Association agents in foreign ports. The *Reports* relate mainly to repairs and alterations to vessels. The *Slips* give details of salvage operations. Both volumes are indexed.

British Corporation Register
The British Corporation Register of Shipping and Aircraft published a *Register of Ships* using its own classifications. With that exception its contents are very similar to those of *Lloyd's Register* with which it was amalgamated in 1949. We have the 1940 volume.

Liverpool Underwriters' list of Iron Vessels
The Underwriters' Registry for Iron Vessels in Liverpool published an *Underwriters' list of Iron Vessels, showing the Class of those which have been Surveyed by the Liverpool Registry*. We have the volume for 1875/6.

41. Wreck Register

The Wreck Register was compiled by a member of Lloyd's staff and comprises miscellaneous lists of wrecks (mainly of the nineteenth and twentieth centuries) round the coasts of Great Britain, Ireland, Iceland, India and the Falkland Islands, arranged alphabetically by area. Dates and positions (where known) are given. For some years typewritten lists of wrecks, arranged by position, have been inserted. It is highly selective, gives minimal information and is of very limited value.

42. Research Boxes, Miscellaneous Files and Scrap Books

Among the ancillary material in the Collection are a number of miscellaneous files of information, some on individual vessels and others on more general subjects. They vary a great deal in size and content, but many consist of copies of correspondence, press cuttings, press releases or offprints from periodicals. The majority are kept in the 'Research boxes', which may be ordered in the usual way. Please consult the staff at the Printed Books Enquiry Desk if you require one of the separate 'miscellaneous' files or scrap books.

Research Box 1
1. Movements of steel barque *Lingard*, 1893 to 1925.
2. Loss of *Allegheny*, in collision with *Caucase*, 1894.
3. Losses of *L'Oriflamme*, 1897, and *Spondilus*, 1912.
4. Vessels seized by Japanese, 1904-5.
5. Vessels seized by the Russians, 1904-5.
6. Loss of *England's Glory*, 1881.
7. Movements of *Mount Stewart*, 1914 to 1923.
8. Loss of *General Turner*, mined 1921.
9. Losses of *George L Munro*, 1920, *Ethel*, 1925, and *Braedale*, 1932.
10. Ice incidents, 1882 to 1968.
11. Vessels trading between Whitehaven and Virginia, 1782-5.
12. Texas City explosions, 1947.
13. Supposed loss of *Santa Cruz*, early C19th.
14. Casualties on River Thames, April 1933 to March 1938.
15. *Ondine* (cross-Channel packet), connection with *The Times*, c.1846.
16. Vessels in collision on River Thames, 1936.
17. Lists of vessels involved in Dunkirk evacuation ('Operation Dynamo'), June 1940. (Superseded by the *Dunkirk List* by G. P. Orde.)
18. Convict ship *Success* (built 1790).
19. Loss of *Egypt* and details of salvage, 1922 to 1939.
20. Survivors of *Strathmore*, lost 1875, and *Diego*, lost 1935.
21. Cargo claims for *Carlo, Eumaeus, Lugano* and *Oronsa* (First World War losses).
22. Tasmania, movements and casualties 1819-24.
23. Activities of German raiders during First World War.
24. Press cuttings etc. on Arab-Israeli dispute, Suez Canal, 1967.
25. *Mary Rose* excavations, 1979 to 1982.

Research Box 2
1. Report of rescue of crew of *Antinoe* by men of *President Roosevelt*, 1926.
2. Loss of *Roumania*, 1892.
3. Loss of *Asturia*, 1901.
4. US wooden steamers abandoned, foundered and missing, 1918-21.
5. Strandings in Kiel Canal, Elbe and Weser, 1923-4.
6. Effects of severe storms in Western Mediterranean, April 1927: *Collingdale, Nicolaos Pateras* and others.
7. Salvage of Greek vessel, lost c.242 BC, in 1958.
8. Casualties in North Sea, English Channel and North Atlantic, 6-14 November 1936.
9. Vessels attacked by aircraft in Spanish and surrounding waters 1 September 1937 to 9 June 1938.
10. Stranding of USS *Richard Montgomery*, 1944, and subsequent history.
11. Collisions in Thames Estuary, 1923-7.
12. Wooden or composite steamers and auxiliary vessels lost by fire while laid up, 1919 to 1925.
13. Loss of *Tubantia*, torpedoed 1916.
14. Vessels of J.H. Bennett Ltd (built 1876 to 1899); *India, Vril, Ormerod, Cornubia, Pivoc, Cadoc, Coath, Cloch, Mercutio.*

15. Miscellaneous brochures (c. 1950-60): Compagnie Générale Trans-atlantique, Ferguson Brothers, Irish Shipping Ltd, P & O, Palm Line, *Bremen Maru, Canberra, Canton, Carthage, Chusan, Corfu, Himalaya, Iberia, Maloja, Mooltan, Oronsay, Siren.*
16. Theft of *Girl Pat*, 1936.
17. Salvage operations on *Grosvenor*, lost 1782.
18. Work on *Kong Haakon VII*, following explosion 1969.
19. Work on *Mactra*, following explosion 1969.
20. Miscellaneous items on Spanish Civil War.
21. 'Royal Navy, 1982'. Presidential address to Institute of Marine Engineers (1982) and leaflets from Royal Navy Presentation Team.

Research Box 3
1. An inventory of the objects recovered from the site of the wreck of the Galleass *Girona* by the Robert Sténuit expedition (1968-9).
2. Vessels reported having struck mines 1958-68 inclusive.
3. Cornish shipwrecks 1800 to 1837.
4. *Royal Charter.*
5. *Banshee* — handbill for voyage to Australia (n.d.)
6. Passenger list of RMS *German*, 1879.
7. Artefacts recovered from S.S. *Medina*.
8. S.S. *Politician*: salvage operations.
9. *Minnehaha*: 1915 passenger list.
10. Loss of the *Tartar*, 1843.
11. *Persia*: 1852 passenger's log.
12. *Arbella*, 1630.
13. San Francisco/Monterey photographic collections.
14. *Central America*: legal ruling on cargo.
15. RGSS records.
16. *Ceramic*, 7.12.1942.
17. Imperial War Museum records.
18. Thames barges.
19. Capt James Waddell of Leith.
20. Tyne & Wear shipbuilding records.
21. Ship losses 1971.
22. RGSS records (*Maritime History* vol. 2 no 2).
23. Lloyd's of London Press.

Miscellaneous files
Bermuda Triangle.
Bombay Dock explosion, 1944.
Admiral Karpfanger, missing 1938.
Salvage on HMS *Dartmouth*, wrecked 1690.
Great Britain, launched 1843, restored 1970 onwards.
Joyita, abandoned 1955.
Kobenhavn, missing 1928.
Lusitania, torpedoed 1915.
Mary Celeste, abandoned 1872.
Salvage of *Niagara*, mined 1940.

Oceana, lost in collision with *Pisagua*, 1912.
Pamir, lost 1957.
Titanic, lost 1912.
Waratah, missing 1909.
Ocean Monarch, burned 1848.

Scrap Books

There are two scrap books, one of them known (though it is not clear why) as the 'Ghosts book' and the other, more prosaically, as the 'Scrap book'. They consist chiefly of newspaper cuttings and press releases on ships and shipping, particularly casualties and 'mysteries', those in the former mainly dating from the 1920s and early 1930s and those in the latter from the period 1956 to 1977. Both are indexed.

43. Book Collection

A small library of books and pamphlets was deposited with the Lloyd's Marine Collection and new items are added to it from time to time. The collection consists mainly of fleet histories, works on particular trades or types of vessel and published accounts of shipwrecks in various parts of the world. The books are included in the Library catalogue, together with many other items on the same and related subjects, which are not part of the Lloyd's Marine Collection.

PART TWO—

MAKING A SEARCH

Part Two of this guide is arranged under broad subject headings and combines checklists of sources in the Lloyd's Marine Collection with notes on those and other sources available in Guildhall Library and elsewhere. The checklists are intended as general guidelines only and readers are advised to consult the full description of each source in Part One before beginning a search (section numbers are shown in brackets). While it is hoped that references to other institutions and organisations in the field will be useful to readers, no attempt has been made to offer a comprehensive guide to sources for maritime history. Where such references have been made, full addresses will be found in the Appendix.

Readers are encouraged to make use of the catalogues of Guildhall Library's own collections and to consult the staff on duty at the enquiry desks. Although the Lloyd's Marine Collection offers an extensive set of records concerned with merchant shipping, it is important that those using Lloyd's records are aware of the wide scope of Guildhall Library's own collections. Since the library is concerned with London history and English local studies, there is inevitably material of interest to the maritime researcher. Printed books on national, local and economic history, topography, biography and Parliamentary Papers will include useful source material. More particularly references to merchant shipping, shipwrecks, books on individual ships or company and fleet histories will be found by searching the Online Public Access Catalogue by author, title, keyword, subject or class mark.

1. Merchant Ships and Shipping

1.1 Ships

Basic sources:
> Lloyd's Register of Shipping (1764 to date minus 2 years) **(1)**
> Mercantile Navy List (British only; 1857-1940; 1947-76) (with monthly supplements 1947-77) **(5)**

Alternatives:
> Parliamentary Papers (lists of steamships 1814-1870) **(1)**

For yachts:
> Lloyd's Register of Yachts (1919-80) **(3)**
> Lloyd's Register of American Yachts (US & Canadian only; 1929-77) **(4)**

All of these, except the Parliamentary Papers, are annual publications listing all vessels (within the limitations of their coverage) afloat at the time of publication. In order to establish the period of service of a vessel, together with any changes of master, owner, flag, etc. which might have occurred, it is often necessary to search through a considerable number of volumes.

Prior to the issue of 1890/1, *Lloyd's Register of Shipping* was largely, though not exclusively, confined to British vessels. The Lloyd's Marine Collection does not include any comprehensive source of information on foreign registered vessels before that date.

1.2 Shipping Movements

Basic source:
> *Lloyd's List* (1741 to date minus three months) **(11)**, used with annual indexes (1838-1927) **(12)** and 'Voyage Record Cards' (1927-c. 1975) **(13)**

Alternatives:
> *Lloyd's Shipping Index* (1880 to within 5 years) **(14)**
> *Lloyd's Voyage Record* (1946 to within 5 years) **(15)**

Additional sources:
> *Lloyd's List Supplementary Mail Advices* (1926-65) **(18)**
> *Yacht and Whaler Movements* (1946 (whalers 1955)-1973) **(21)**
> *Vessels on Government Service* (1914-18 (microfilm), 1939-45) **(14)**
> Lloyd's *Confidential Sheets* (1939-45) **(19)**
> *Troopships that survived the War*. MT 40 **(20)**
> 'Confidential Movements of Vessels on Special Government Service' Notebooks, 1939-45 **(19)**.

The most usual method of tracing the movements of named vessels before the period covered by the 'Voyage Record Cards' is to use *Lloyd's List* in conjunction with its annual indexes, although after 1908 the indexes can in some circumstances stand on their own. Bear in mind that before that date the indexes give only references to *Lloyd's List*, not the actual dates of sailings and arrivals, and that, particularly in the earlier part of the period, reports often appeared in *Lloyd's List* a long time after the event. Like the later indexes, the 'Voyage Record Cards' give actual dates of movements and can usually be used without reference to *Lloyd's List* itself. We do, however, require a minimum of 48 hours' notice to get them out. *Lloyd's Shipping Index* offers more immediate access to dates of sailing and arrival after 1880, but should be treated with some caution as it does not necessarily record every port of call.

Lloyds List reports sailings and arrivals port by port and is therefore a convenient source in which to search if you do not know the name of the vessel in which you are interested. Allow for some delay in reporting: all sailings or arrivals which occurred on the same day at the same port would not necessarily have been reported in the same issue of *Lloyd's List*.

1.3 Shipping Losses (other than war losses)

Basic sources:
> *Lloyd's List* (1741 to date minus three months) **(11)** used with partial indexes to 1838, annual index (1838-1927) **(12)** and 'Voyage Record

Cards' (1927-c.1975) (**13**)
Lloyd's Shipping Index (1880-1917) (**14**)
Lloyd's Weekly Casualty Reports (1920-85) (**16**)

Alternatives:
Lloyd's 'Subscription Books' (1774-1849) (**33**) (Mss Section)
Lloyd's 'Loss and Casualty Books' (1837-1980) (**34**) (Mss Section)
'Lloyd's Missing Vessels Books' (1873-1954) (**35**)
'Marine Loss Cards' (c. 1939-1972) (**28**) (N.B. 48 hours' notice required)

Additional sources:
Board of Trade casualty returns (1879/80-1918) (**24**)
Registrar General's monthly returns (1890-1946) (**6**)
Bureau Veritas publications (1896-1938) (**25**)
Lloyd's Register Casualty Returns (1890-1980) (**2**)
Lloyd's Confidential Index 'Cemetery cards' (c.1920-c.1976) (**38**)
Liverpool Underwriters' casualty returns (1934-9, 1946-80) (**26**)
Lloyd's *Confidential sheets* (1939-45) (**19**)
Lloyd's Total Loss Returns (1947-69) (**27**)
Board of Trade. *Wreck Registers U.K.* 1855-1898 (**23**)
The Times Index 1785-date.

For more detailed accounts:
Board of Trade inquiry reports (for 1880-1920 summaries in *Lloyd's List Weekly Summary* (**17**), 1908-65 separate file (**29**)), Parliamentary Papers 1856-76

For geographical approach:
Wreck Register (**41**)

Searching for a named and dated wreck is relatively straightforward, although the amount of information to be found can vary enormously. In general, reports in *Lloyd's List* tended to become fuller over the years, particularly after the introduction of telegraphic communications, which made it possible to convey on-the-spot reports to London very rapidly. Only rarely, however, do reports include detailed descriptions of cargoes or name crew members or passengers (either victims or survivors). For wrecks after 1920 it is normally best to use *Lloyd's Weekly Casualty Reports* which contain all the reports previously published in *Lloyd's List* in a more manageable format and, more importantly, with a quarterly index. Fuller particulars of a casualty can sometimes be found in Board of Trade inquiry reports, when available. Those for the period 1908 to 1965 can be seen at Guildhall Library with summaries from 1856-80. There is a full set at the Department of Transport Marine Library. Occasionally, for example in the case of a major disaster, a report would be presented to Parliament, in which case it will be found among the Parliamentary Papers in the Library's own collections. The library has a virtually complete set of House of Commons Papers from 1801 to date, as well as some earlier reports. Indexes may be consulted at the Printed Books Enquiry Desk.

Finding information on an unnamed or undated wreck can be more difficult. Apart from the very sketchy 'Wreck Register' there is no geographical index to wrecks in the Collection, although the library does have a number of books on the wrecks of particular areas. The Wreck Section of the Hydrographic Department has a computer index of wrecks around the British Isles and other continental shelf areas (mostly post-1900) and there is also a privately-owned UK Shipwreck Computer Index which aims eventually to list all known wrecks around the coast of the British Isles since 1100 AD. Within the Lloyd's Marine Collection, the 'Loss and Casualty Books' are usually the best source in which to look for an unnamed or undated wreck, as long as the probable period within which it occurred is not too long. The 'Loss Books' themselves are arranged chronologically and the entries usually indicate approximate locations. Each year is indexed separately, alphabetically by name of vessel. Named but undated wrecks for the period since 1939 can be traced through the 'Marine Loss Cards'.

Enquirers are often anxious to trace the present-day owners of wrecks which sank at some time in the past, but this is something in which the Lloyd's Marine Collection can be of little help as there are no insurance records in the Collection. In rare cases it is possible for the brokers concerned in a post-1939 loss to be identified from the 'Marine Loss Cards' and on these occasions further information may be available from the firm. The Salvage Association can some-times assist, but is mainly concerned to protect the interests of owners of hull or cargo where commercial salvage is in view. Members of the British Sub-Aqua Club should approach the Salvage Association through BS-AC headquarters.

1.4 War Losses

1.4.1. First World War (1914-18)

Basic sources:
> *Lloyd's War Losses: the First World War* (1990 reprint) **(30)**

Additional sources:
> Lloyd's 'War Casualty Books' (1914-22; indexed 1917-22) **(34)** (Mss Section)
> *Lloyd's Shipping Index* (1914-17) **(14)**
> *Lloyd's List* (1914-16) **(11)**
> *Oversea Shipping Intelligence* (1917-November 1918) **(11)**
> Spindler, A. *Der Handelskrieg mit U Booten/The Submarine War against Commerce* **(32)**
> *Lloyd's Prizes of War* **(32)**
> Ministry of Shipping. Shipping Intelligence Section. *Service List — World War One* **(32)**
> Board of Trade. *Government War Risks Insurance Scheme. List of Vessels Lost, Damaged or Missing* **(32)**
> Tennent, A. J. *British Merchant Ships Sunk by U-Boats during the 1914-1918 War* **(32)**

Lloyd's 'Return of Ships sunk during the Great War' (32)
Admiralty. *Merchant Shipping (Losses)* (1919) (32)
Admiralty. *Navy Losses* (1919) (32)

For missing vessels:
'Vessels against which closing entries have been made in the Daily Index'
(1916-April 1925) (35)

See also Part One, Section 32, 'Other sources of information on war losses'.

1.4.2. Spanish Civil War (1936-9)

Basic source:
Lloyd's Confidential Index microfilm index of losses (38)

Additional sources:
Vessels attacked by aircraft in Spanish and surrounding waters
1 September 1937 to 9 June 1938 (Research Box 2, Item 9) (42)
Miscellaneous items on Spanish Civil War (Research Box 2, Item 20) (42)

1.4.3. Sino-Japanese War (1937- 9)

Basic source:
Lloyd's Confidential Index microfilm index of losses (38)

1.4.4. Second World War (1939-45)

Basic sources:
Lloyd's War Losses: the Second World War. Vols 1-3 (1989-93 reprint).
(30)
'War Loss Cards' (31) (N.B. 48 hours' notice required)

Additional sources:
Lloyd's Weekly Casualty Reports (16)
Lloyd's List (11)
Lloyd's *Confidential Sheets* (19)
Orde, G. P. *Dunkirk withdrawal, Operation Dynamo* (32)
Rohwer, J. *Die U Boot erfolge der Achsenmachte 1939-45/Axis submarine successes 1939-45* (32)
Ministry of War Transport. *Small Craft Service List.* (32)
Ministry of War Transport. *Service List* (32)
Admiralty. *British Merchant Vessels Lost or Damaged by Enemy Action during Second World War* (32)
Admiralty. *Ships of the Royal Navy: Statement of losses during the Second World War* (32)

For missing vessels:
'Vessels against which closing entries have been made in the Daily Index' (1941-January 1946) **(35)**

See also Part One, Section 32, 'Other sources of information on war losses'.

Information on ownership of vessels sunk in the First and Second World Wars can be obtained from the Department of Transport, Domestic Shipping Policy Emergencies Division.

2. People and Firms

2.1 Masters and Mates

Apart from the lists of qualified mates which appear in *Lloyd's Register* (1846-52) and the *Mercantile Navy List* (1857-64), the Lloyd's Marine Collection includes no records of seamen below the level of master mariner.

Basic source:
Lloyd's 'Captains Registers' (1869, but including some retrospective details, -1948, plus a few 'Confidential Circulars' 1900-46) **(36)** (Mss Section)

Additional sources:
Lloyd's Register of Shipping (1846-52) **(1)**
Mercantile Navy List (1857-64) **(5)**

For details of suspensions:
Lloyd's Confidential Index (1886-1919) **(37)**

The 'Captains Registers' record the careers of master mariners who were active between 1868 and 1948. They were based on information supplied by the Registrar General of Shipping and Seamen from his registers of masters' certificates. These registers, which contain similar information to the 'Captains Registers' at Guildhall Library, though arranged in a different order, are retained by the Registrar General for the period since c. 1900. Earlier registers (1845-c. 1900) are now held by the Public Record Office. Registers of mates', engineers' and certain other certificates are similarly divided between the Registrar General and the Public Record Office. Applications for examination and copies of all classes of certificates of competency or service, 1850-c.1926/7, are at the National Maritime Museum, Greenwich. The Registrar General retains those for the twentieth century.

2.2 Crew

Crew lists from 1835 onwards, and the muster rolls (1747 onwards) which preceded them, are now deposited in a number of places although there are none in the Lloyd's Marine Collection.

1747-1860

All surviving crew lists, crew agreements or muster rolls for British registered merchant ships up to and including 1860 are held by the Public Record Office, Ruskin Avenue, Kew, Richmond, Surrey TW9 4DU. After this date, they are divided between a number of repositories.

1861-1938

10% of crew agreements for each year, together with those for famous vessels, have been retained by the Public Record Office. The remaining 90% for 1861, 1862, and years ending in '5', are held at the National Maritime Museum, Greenwich. They are held at an outstation, so that visitors wishing to consult them must give advance notice of at least a week, in order for them to be made available. For other years, some crew agreements have been taken by local record offices, and all those remaining, about 70% of the total, are now in the care of the Maritime History Archive, Memorial University of Newfoundland, St John's, Newfoundland, A1C 5S7, Canada.

1939-1950

All crew agreements are held by the General Register and Record Office of Shipping and Seamen, Block 2, Government Buildings, St Agnes Road, Gabalfa, Cardiff CF4 4YA.

1951-1978

10% of crew agreements have been retained by the Public Record Office, and the remaining 90% for years ending in '5' have been deposited with the National Maritime Museum. Those for 1965 and 1975 are currently held in a Public Record Office store and are not available to the public. All remaining papers have been transferred to the Maritime History Archive in Canada.

1979 onwards

All crew lists are held by the General Register and Record Office of Shipping and Seamen. Further deposits to the Public Record Office, National Maritime Museum, and Maritime History Archive, may be made at intervals. Papers may be temporarily unavailable while in transit.

Indexes

The Maritime History Archive has produced indexes to its holdings, covering 1863-1913 and 1914-1938, arranged by ship's official number. A similar index has been compiled to the papers held by local record offices; and one is in preparation to the holdings of the Public Record Office. No indexes by ship's name or by the names of crewmen have yet been compiled to the three main collections, although some local record offices have got indexes by ship's name to their holdings. The official number of a ship can be found by consulting the *Mercantile Navy List* or, after 1872/3, *Lloyd's Register of Shipping*.

Official logs

British merchant ships were first required to keep an official log under the Merchant Shipping Act of 1850; and logs start to appear amongst official records from 1852 onwards. They were normally retained only if they recorded a birth, marriage or death on board, the survival rate being about 20%. Those that do survive are always to be found with the appropriate crew agreement. The index to the Maritime History Archive's holdings of crew agreements from 1914 to 1938 indicates whether or not a log is available with the crew agreement. The official log is not a deck log, and seldom includes information about the navigation of a vessel. Its function is to record vital information relating to the crew and passengers, such as disciplinary action taken against crew members, new arrivals on board (such as a birth, or the signing on of a new crew member) or departures (death, disappearance, desertion, the signing off of a crew member at an intermediary port before the end of the voyage, etc). The log will usually give the ship's position at the time of any birth, marriage or death on board, or other departure or arrival. Sailing and arrival dates are sometimes given, but were not required. The date and place of the beginning and end of the voyage will be given on the crew agreement. Copies of deck logs or journals survive only in rare instances, and are not amongst the official records. The National Maritime Museum's manuscripts collections include a few examples.

2.2.1 Wills of Seamen

The wills of some Royal Naval and merchant seamen were proved in the Commissary Court of London (London Division) and survive among its records in the Manuscripts Section of the Library. Those of Royal Naval seamen come from the period of the late seventeenth to the mid-eighteenth centuries and those of merchant seamen from the late seventeenth century to 1857. Before 1858 the majority of seamen's wills would have been proved in the Prerogative Court of Canterbury, the records of which are held at the Public Record Office, Chancery Lane, London WC2A ILR. All wills proved since 1858 are held at the Principal Registry, Family Division, Somerset House, Strand, London WC2R ILP. (For burials at sea, see page 47, 2.3.1).

2.3 Passengers

There are no passenger lists in the Lloyd's Marine Collection and indeed virtually no original lists survive in this country from the period before 1890, apart from a few relating to vessels arriving in the United Kingdom between 1878 and 1888. These, and the surviving lists for the period between 1890 and 1960, are held at the Public Record Office. It is normally necessary to know the name of the vessel and the date and port of sailing in order to undertake a search.

Although there are no passenger lists in the Lloyd's Marine Collection, the Library does have a number of books which list emigrants, mainly to America. References to them will be found in the General Subject Catalogue at 325.2. Among the most important for America are: *Passenger and Immigration Lists Index* compiled by P. William Filby and Mary K. Meyer (3 vols, 1981 and supplements, annually) which covers immigrants into the United States and Canada in the seventeenth, eighteenth and nineteenth centuries; J.C. Hotten's *The Original Lists of Persons of Quality*; emigrants who went from Great Britain to the American plantations, 1600-1700 (1931) (325/2); Carl Boyer's series of *Ship Passenger Lists*, covering the South (1538-1825), New York and New Jersey (1600-1825), Pennsylvania and Delaware (1641-1825) and national and New England (1600-1825) (325/2); and P.W. Coldham's *Bonded Passengers to America* (1983), which lists convicts (365). Filby and Meyer's sources are listed in *Passenger and Immigration Lists Bibliography, 1538-1900* (1981), which is the most comprehensive list of published sources for American immigrants (R325/2). However, the majority of the sources listed are American publications, often local and family history society periodicals, which are not available at Guildhall Library. Australia is represented by *The First Fleeters: a comprehensive listing of convicts, mariners, seamen, officers, wives, children and ships* compiled by Paul G. Fidlon and R.J. Ryan (1981) (325/94) and the *Dictionary of Western Australians, 1829-1914*, general editor Rica Erickson, (in progress, 1981—) (325/941) and South Africa by Peter Philip's *British Residents at the Cape, 1795-1819: biographical records of 4800 pioneers . . .* (1981) (920/096) and *British Settlers in Natal, 1824-1857: a biographical register* by Shelagh O'Byrne Spencer (in progress, 1981 —) (325/684).

2.3.1 Baptisms, Marriages and Burials at Sea

The London Diocesan archives held in the Manuscripts Section include records of some baptisms (1810, 1822, 1860-1952 and 1955-61) and burials (1860-1952) at sea. Records of some marriages which took place on Royal Naval ships only during the period 1842 to 1879 may also be found. The records at Guildhall Library are incomplete. For births and deaths at sea from 1837 it is normally advisable to consult the Marine Register at the General Register Office, St. Catherines House, 10 Kingsway, London WC2B 6JP. Sources of information in this field, both at Guildhall Library and elsewhere are described more fully in *The British Overseas: a guide to records of their births, baptisms, marriages, deaths and burials available in the United Kingdom*, compiled by Geoffrey Yeo (Guildhall Library, 1988). Another useful reference work is *My Ancestor was a Merchant Seaman: how can I find out more about him?* by C. T. and M. J. Watts (1986).

2.4 Shipowners

Basic sources:
   Lloyd's Register of Shipping (1876/7-to date minus 2 years) **(1)**
   Lloyd's Confidential Index (1886 (steam), 1894 (sail) to 30 years before current date) **(37)**

Brief histories of a number of British shipping companies, together with descriptions of their archives, will be found in *Shipping: a survey of historical records* edited by P. Mathias and A.W.H. Pearsall (1971). The aforementioned work is rather out of date now and the following titles are more worthy of consideration: *British archives, a guide to archive resources in the United Kingdom* by Janet Foster and Julia Shepherd (1989) and *Directory of corporate archives* compiled by Lesley Richmond and Alison Turton (1992).

The National Register of Archives is an organisation which is concerned with the identification, care and storage of business records. The address is Quality House, Quality Court, London WC2. The Lloyd's collection of books (see Part One, Section 43) includes a number of published histories of shipping companies, as do the Library's own collections.

2.5 Shipbuilders

Basic source:
   Lloyd's Register of Shipping (1890/1 to date minus 2 years) **(1)**

Brief histories of a number of British shipbuilding companies, together with descriptions of their archives, will be found in *The Shipbuilding Industry: A guide to historical records* edited by L. A. Ritchie (1992).

3. Royal Navy

A few issues of *Lloyd's Register* (1779 to 1783 and 1890/1 to 1894/5 only) and the *Mercantile Navy List* (1857 to 1864, 1869 and 1871 only) contain lists of Royal Naval vessels, and until the middle of the nineteenth century *Lloyd's List* sometimes published brief reports of naval engagements and of the movements of Royal Naval vessels. The Library has J.J. Colledge's *Ships of the Royal Navy* (2 vols 1969-87), which aims to be a comprehensive list of Royal Naval vessels from the fifteenth century to the time of publication, a set of *Jane's Fighting Ships* (1898 to date) and an extensive collection of *Navy Lists* from 1793 onwards, in addition to many secondary sources on the subject. Complementary to the *Navy Lists* is *Commissioned Sea Officers of the Royal Navy 1660-1815* (1954) (923/5) and there are several eighteenth and nineteenth century biographical dictionaries of serving Royal Naval officers. The number in the General Subject Catalogue for naval history is 359.09 and the number for naval biography 923.5. The archives of the Admiralty, including personnel records, described in detail in *Naval records for genealogists* by N.A.M. Rodger (1984), are held by the Public Record Office, Ruskin Avenue, Kew, Richmond, Surrey TW9 4DU.

4. East India Company

Between 1778 and 1833 *Lloyd's Register* includes separate lists of East India Company ships. Their movements are reported in *Lloyd's List* in the same way as those of other merchant vessels. Some early issues of the *Mercantile Navy List* (1857-64, 1869 and 1871) list the ships of the East India Company Navy, after

1858 H M Indian Navy. The Library holds a great deal of printed material relating to the East India Company, both contemporary and secondary sources. References will be found in the London Subject Catalogue at the numbers L63.3 and L63.301. The most useful sources of information on the Company's ships are Charles Hardy's *A Register of Ships Employed in the Service of the . . . East India Company from the year 1760 (to 1833)* (1835) (LB 268) and *An Analysis of One Hundred Voyages to and from India, China, etc. performed by Ships in the Honourable East India Company's Service* by Henry Wise (1839) (S623/87). The archives of the Company are held by the Oriental and India Office Collections, The British Library, 197 Blackfriars Road, London SE1 8NG.

5. Insurance Records

There are no insurance records in the Lloyd's Marine Collection. Records of transactions are the responsibility of the firms concerned and are not kept centrally by Lloyd's. Some suggestions on tracing current owners of wrecks are made in sections **1.3 Shipping Losses (other than war losses)** and **1.4 War Losses above.**

The marine insurance business is not confined to members of Lloyd's. The Manuscripts Section holds the records of a number of other firms involved in marine insurance, including Royal Exchange Assurance (from 1720), the London Assurance Corporation (from 1720), Indemnity Marine Insurance Co. Ltd (from 1824), Alliance Assurance Co. (from 1824) and Ocean Marine Insurance Co. Ltd (from 1859). These records appear in the London Subject Catalogue in the Manuscripts Reading Room at the number L64.9. While the minute books and other records relating to company policy are of value to the business historian, the information on individual risks is generally confined to short periods, presumably determined by the accidental survival of certain volumes, and, when traceable, is very limited in scope.

Further information on insurance companies and their surviving records may be found in *The British Insurance Business 1547-1970: an introduction and guide to historical records in the United Kingdom* by H.A.L. Cockerell and Edwin Green (1976), of which copies are available both in the Printed Books Section (368) and at the Manuscripts Enquiry Desk.

6. Pictures

There is no collection of illustrations among Lloyd's Marine Records. The National Maritime Museum holds extensive collections of paintings, prints, drawings and photographs of ships and is probably the best place to begin a search. Two volumes of the Museum's *General catalogue of historic photographs*, volume one *Warship photographs (Richard Perkins Collection)* and volume two *Merchant sailing ships*, have been published and are available in the Library. Other important works produced by the Museum include a *Concise catalogue of oil paintings in the National Maritime Museum* compiled by the staff of the Museum (1988), *Portraits at the National Maritime Museum* selected by E.H.H. Archibald (2 vols 1954-5) and *Steam and Sail in Britain and North America — 80 photographs mainly from the National Maritime Museum depicting British and North American naval, merchant and special purpose vessels of the period of transition from sail to steam* (1973).

The World Ship Society, Department SB, 5 Grove Road, Walton Le Dale, Preston, Lancashire has a catalogue of its holdings of photographs of merchant ships. It is in the form of a computer catalogue.

Within the Library's general collections there are a number of books that contain illustrations of ships and these books may be identified through the catalogue.

7. Cargoes

There are no cargo manifests in the Lloyd's Marine Collection. Brief references to cargoes may be found in reports of marine losses in *Lloyd's List* and associated publications.

The most likely source for detailed information on cargoes of British vessels is the Custom House at the port of departure or of arrival (in the U.K.). Cargoes for vessels lost by war causes only may be known to the Department of Transport, Domestic Shipping Policy Emergencies Division. They are not concerned with marine losses. The address is Room P1/085, 2 Marsham Street, London, SW1P 3EB.

For information on the current location of the records of any particular Custom House, contact HM Customs and Excise, Departmental Records, Floor 4E, Ralli Quays, 3 Stanley Street, Salford M60 9LA.

APPENDIX

SOURCES OF INFORMATION OUTSIDE GUILDHALL LIBRARY

The following is a list of libraries and other institutions to which we often refer enquirers who are searching for information not provided by the Lloyd's Marine Collection. Additional details about the majority of them (in the form of published catalogues, handlists etc.) are available at Guildhall Library. Readers requiring a full guide to sources of information in this field are referred to *Marine transport: a guide to libraries and sources of information in Great Britain* (Library Association/Marine Librarians' Association, 2nd edition, 1983), a copy of which may be seen at the Printed Books Enquiry Desk.

Department of Transport, Marine Library
105 Commercial Road, Southampton SO1 0ZD.
Telephone: 0703 329100   Steven Grace x293

Access: letter or personal (by prior arrangement), 9.00-4.30 Monday to Friday.

Holdings: published material on administration of the Merchant Shipping Acts from 1855 including boiler explosion reports (1882-1973) and wreck reports (Board of Trade Inquiry reports) (1876 onwards; indexed).

Department of Transport, Domestic Shipping Policy Emergencies Division
Room P1/085, 2 Marsham Street, London SW1P 3EB
Telephone: 071-276 5625

Access: letter or personal (by prior arrangement), 9.00-4.00 Monday to Friday.

Holdings: records of ownership of hull and cargo of Allied merchant ships lost by war causes during the First and Second World Wars (name and date of loss required).

General Register and Record Office of Shipping and Seamen
Block 2, Government Buildings, St Agnes Road, Gabalfa, Cardiff CF4 4YA
Telephone: 0222 586000

Access: Letter or personal (fees payable), 9.30-4.30 Monday-Friday.

Holdings: UK Registry of Ships (of all sizes)
            Records of ordinary seamen 1870 onwards

Records of officers 1913 onwards
Births and Deaths at Sea 1891 onwards
Crew Lists 1979 onwards
Index to Ships' Official Number

Lloyd's Register of Shipping, Information Group
71 Fenchurch Street, London EC3M 4BS
Telephone: 071-709 9166 extension 2475 or 2531

Access: letter or personal, 9.30-4.30 Monday to Friday.

Holdings: include complete sets of *Lloyd's Register, Lloyd's Register of
             Yachts* and other publications of Lloyd's Register of Shipping,
             together with a small reference Library.

Maritime History Archive, Memorial University of Newfoundland
St. John's, Newfoundland, Canada A1C 5S7

Access: by letter (search fee charged) or personal.

Holdings: crew lists, agreements and official logs of British vessels, 1863-
             1939 and 1951-1976 (currently indexed to 1938) other than those
             held at the PRO, NMM and local record offices. Additional trans-
             fers of records from the RGSS are made at regular intervals.

Ministry of Defence (Navy), Hydrographic Office, Wreck Section.
Taunton, Somerset TA1 2DN
Telephone: 0823 87900, extension 381 or 323

Access: by letter only (search fee charged).

Holdings: computer index of all reported wrecks around the British Isles;
             computer index of wrecks elsewhere in areas for which the United
             Kingdom is still considered to have primary charting responsibility
             (mainly post 1900).

National Maritime Museum
Romney Road, Greenwich, London SE10 9NF
Telephone: 081-858 4422

Access (apart from public galleries, for which an admission fee is charged):
1.   Library. By ticket only, Monday-Friday 10.00-5.00; Saturday by
     appointment 10.00-1.00, 2.00-5.00. Advance notice must usually
     be given for manuscript holdings, the bulk of which are outhoused.
     Enquiries answered by telephone and letter.
2.   Other departments. By appointment.

52

Holdings: library holds c. 100,000 volumes plus 20,000 bound periodicals relating to all aspects of maritime history. Manuscripts holdings include crew lists and official logs for 1861-2, 1865, 1875, 1885, 1895, 1905, 1915, 1925, 1935 and 1955; certificates of competency (with application forms) for masters and other officers, 1850-1926; Lloyd's Register of Shipping survey reports c. 1833-c. 1964; wreck registers 1855-1898; and archives of various shipowners and shipbuilders, including P & O and Denny of Dumbarton. Other departments cover historic photographs, paintings, prints and drawings; ships' plans; weapons and antiquities etc.

Oriental and India Office Collections, The British Library
197 Blackfriars Road, London SEI 8NG.
Telephone: 071-412 7873

Access: letter or personal, 9.30-5.45 Monday to Friday; 9.30-1.00 Saturday.

Holdings: include the archives of the East India Company; series on Maritime Service officers; c. 9000 logs and account books (with crew lists) of voyages to Asia 1601-1833; Bombay Marine, Indian Navy personnel and history 1750-1947.

Public Record Office
Ruskin Avenue, Kew, Richmond, Surrey TW9 4DU
Telephone: 081-876 3444

Access: letter or personal (by ticket only), 9.30-5.00 Monday to Friday.

Holdings: include muster rolls 1747-1851; agreements and crew lists 1835-60 (complete) and 10% sample (every tenth box) from 1861-1938; registers of seamen's service 1835-56; registers of masters', mates' and engineers' certificates (c.1845-c.1900); passenger lists (inwards 1878-88 and 1890 onwards, outwards 1890 onwards); correspondence, registers and letter books of the Board of Trade and other government departments concerning mercantile marine matters (c.1850 onwards). PRO leaflets available at Guildhall Library.

The Salvage Association
Bankside House, 107-112 Leadenhall Street, London EC3A 4AP

Access: available to salvors only (by letter). Members of the British Sub-Aqua Club should contact BS-AC headquarters.

Holdings: the Association "protects the interests of beneficiaries still concerned with sunken ships and/or cargo and maintains records of losses for that purpose". (Name and date of loss required).

United Kingdom Shipwreck Index
Ropewalk House, Charlestown, St. Austell, Cornwall PL25 3NN
Telephone: 0726 73104

Access: by letter only, enclosing a stamped addressed envelope with details. Information for individual vessels up to ten can be made available, but not for complete areas. In most cases where data is available, a search fee will be charged.

Holdings: The UK Shipwreck Computer Index is a private initiative which has the ultimate aim of listing all known shipwrecks around the coast of the United Kingdom and Ireland from 1100 AD to the present day. 52 "fields" of information constitute a full wreck entry, including 16 lines of text and bibliography, and for 19th-20th century losses are often complete. In the cases of early losses there may be only basic details, since very little else is usually available. The Index is working anticlockwise around the country, starting with the Isles of Scilly, is county based to 30 miles offshore, and is chronological.

GLOSSARY

Captain — 1) RN: rank next above Commander.
2) See **Master**.

Casualty — 1) A lost or damaged vessel.
2) Loss of or damage to a vessel.

Flag — Nationality (i.e. country in which a vessel is registered).

Marine loss — Loss of vessel due to foundering, stranding, collision etc., as distinct from **War loss**.

Master — 1) The commander of a merchant vessel; used inter-changeably with 'captain'.
2) Abbreviation of 'master mariner', i.e. a person qualified by apprenticeship or examination to command a merchant vessel.
3) RN: officer responsible solely for navigation of a warship (obs).

Missing vessel — One which disappears without trace, as distinct from one whose fate is known.

Posting — Hand-printed amendment to *Lloyd's Register of Shipping* recording loss, breaking up etc.

Speaking — (Report of) communication with another vessel at sea.

War Loss — Loss of vessel due to enemy causes (submarines, mines, bombing, etc.), as distinct from **Marine Loss**.

INDEX

The index covers Parts One and Two, but does not include references to the Appendix or Glossary.

In Part One, Section 42 (pages 36-38), the contents of the Research Boxes and Miscellaneous Files are listed. In the index references to them in the Research Boxes show the box and item numbers prefixed by the letters 'RB' (eg 'RB' 1/3 = Research Box 1, item 3). References to items in the Miscellaneous Files, which are not numbered, are indicated by the letters 'MF'.

56

57